130 Great Irish Ballads

INTRODUCTION

I started working on this book almost two years ago. The idea sprang out of my love of music - traditional Irish music and ballads in particular.

Each of these songs I have sung at one time or another in the past. Usually in pubs. A sure sign of a mis-spent youth! But what a way to mis-spend it! The songs are ever present all around me - on faded bits of paper, in my head, captured in the soundbox of my guitar and banjo.

So I decided to compile them into one book - my version of the songs, the lyrics, the guitar chords - and here it is!

Although all of these songs are 'great Irish ballads' it's fair to say that a small number of them originated in other lands in the dim and distant past. But they have been sung by so many Irish balladeers on so many occasions up and down the length and breadth of Ireland that they have been adopted as full-blooded Irish ballads. They have found their natural home!

So enjoy these songs! Sing them! Change the words or music or timing if you feel something else works better for you! After all, that's what ballads are all about!

A Big Thank You

There are many people who encouraged and helped me with this book. I would like to thank Trish Ryan, Sharon Murphy and Dec "I'll get this C diminished to work if it kills me" O'Brien for all of the practical help they gave me.

But in particular I would like to give special thanks to Karen O'Mahony from the Mechanical Copyright Protection Society for the countless hours she spent trying to unravel the maze of copyright control on these songs. Without her help I doubt if this book would exist today.

The CD

If you are not familiar with the particular melody of a song and can't read music the accompanying CD will provide you with the tune. I have coupled some songs together on the CD (marked 'a' and 'b' on the particular tracks) because I think that they go well together – either through the melody, tempo or theme.

The Chorus

If a song has a chorus it is printed in bold italics *like this*. Some songs start with a chorus and therefore it will be in the main body of the score. Others have the chorus after the first verse.

Choruses are great things – they are a law unto themselves. You can add more in (and this normally depends on the number of verses the singer knows!) or take them out if you want to shorten the song. So do your own thing! Do it your way!

But above all, enjoy these songs! They are crying out to be sung!

Robert Gogan
November 1997

INDEX BY SONG

INDEX BY FIRST LINE

Index By CD Track

CD Track	Song Title
1	Star Of The County Down, The
2	Weile Waile
3	Come To The Bower
4	Henry My Son
5 a	I'm A Rover
5 b	Jug Of Punch, The
6	Town Of Ballybay, The
7	Avondale
8 a	Cliffs Of Doneen, The
8 b	Meeting Of The Waters, The
9	Curragh Of Kildare, The
10 a	Galway Races, The
10 b	Bold O'Donoghue
11	Banks Of The Roses, The
12	Monto
13	Arthur McBride
14	Believe Me If All Those Endearing Young Charms
15	Carrickfergus
16	I Know My Love
17	Wearing Of The Green, The
18 a	Glendalough Saint, The
18 b	German Clockwinder, A
19 a	Three Lovely Lassies From Kimmage
19 b	Maids When You're Young
20	Dicey Riley
21	Enniskillen Dragoon, The
22 a	Boston Burglar, The
22 b	Spancil Hill
23	Hills Of Kerry, The
24	Jolly Beggerman, The
25 a	Reilly's Daughter
25 b	Gypsy, The
26	When You Were Sweet Sixteen
27 a	Boulavogue
27 b	Sweet Carnlough Bay
28	Banna Strand
29 a	Wild Rover, The
29 b	Fiddler's Green
30	Bold Thady Quill, The
31	Wild Colonial Boy, The
32	Courtin' In The Kitchen
33	Holy Ground, The
34	She Moved Through The Fair
35	Bunch Of Thyme, A

CD Track	Song Title
36	Croppy Boy, The
37	Joe Hill
38	Merry Ploughboy, The
39 a	Foggy Dew, The
39 b	Minstrel Boy, The
40 a	Black Velvet Band, The
40 b	Look At The Coffin
41	Raggle Taggle Gypsy, The
42	West's Awake, The
43	Easy And Slow
44	Bard Of Armagh, The
45 a	Paddy's Green Shamrock Shore
45 b	Cockles And Mussels
46	Danny Boy – The Derry Air
47	Finnegan's Wake
48	Whiskey In The Jar
49 a	Tipping It Up To Nancy
49 b	Home By Bearna
50	As I Roved Out
51	Rose Of Allendale, The
52	Bonny Boy, The
53 a	Old Woman From Wexford
53 b	All For Me Grog
54 a	Boys From The County Armagh, The
54 b	I Once Loved A Lass
55 a	Moonshiner, The
55 b	Mush Mush
56 a	Spanish Lady, The
56 b	Highland Paddy
57	Skibbereen
58	Leaving Of Liverpool, The
59	Harp That Once Through Tara's Halls, The
60	I Know Where I'm Going
61	Johnny I Hardly Knew Ye
62	Lark In The Morning, The
63	Peggy Gordon
64 a	Shores Of Americay, The
64 b	Nightingale, The
65 a	Roddy McCorley
65 b	Nation Once Again, A
66 a	Let The Grasses Grow
66 b	Rising Of The Moon, The
67	James Connolly
68	Last Rose Of Summer, The
69	Love Is Teasing

CD Track	Song Title
70	Mountains Of Mourne, The
71	Follow Me Up To Carlow
72	O'Donnell Abu
73	Old Maid In The Garret
74 a	Kelly From Killane
74 b	Muirsheen Durkin
75 a	Nora
75 b	Butcher Boy, The
76 a	Banks Of My Own Lovely Lee, The
76 b	Bunclody
77	I Never Will Marry
78	Rocky Road To Dublin, The
79	My Singing Bird
80	Zoological Gardens, The
81 a	Slievenamon
81 b	Snowy Breasted Pearl, The
82 a	Mermaid, The
82 b	Sean South From Garryowen
83	I'll Tell Me Ma
84 a	Boys Of Fairhill, The
84 b	Waxies' Dargle, The
85	Rose Of Mooncoin, The
86	Sally Gardens, The
87 a	Three Score And Ten
87 b	Sam Hall
88	Lanigan's Ball
89 a	Twenty-one Years
89 b	Quare Bungle Rye, The
90	Rosin The Bow
91	Juice Of The Barley, The
92 a	Galway Shawl, The
92 b	Banks Of Claudy, The
93	Paddy Lay Back
94 a	Let Him Go, Let Him Tarry
94 b	Golden Jubilee, The
95	Scariff Martyrs, The
96	Rose Of Tralee, The
97	Rocks Of Bawn, The
98 a	Brennan On The Moor
98 b	Botany Bay
99	Red Is The Rose

Guitar chords used in this book

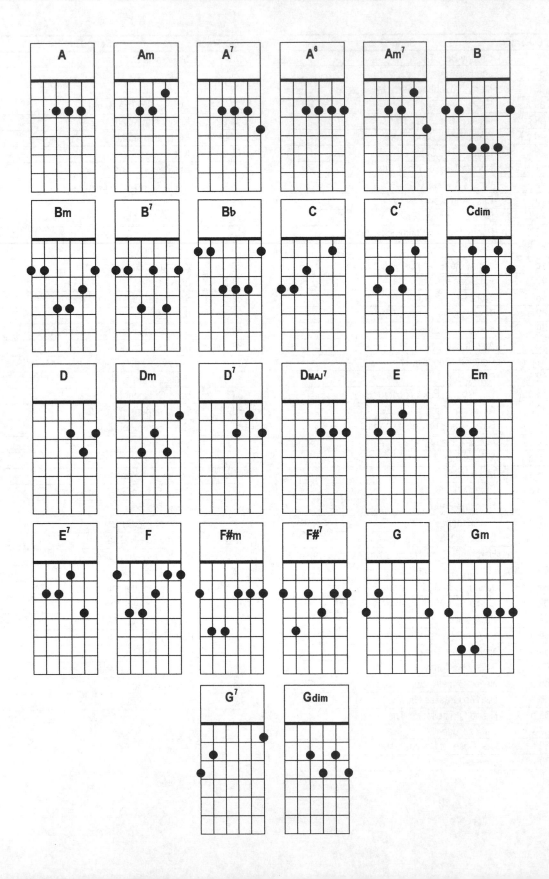

James Connolly

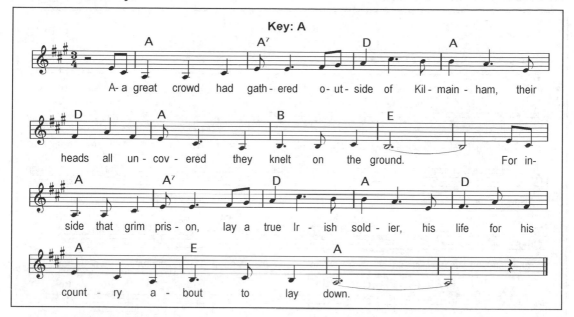

He went to his death like a true son of Erin
The firing party he bravely did face
Then the order rang out "Present arms" and "Fire!"
James Connolly fell into a ready made grave

The black flag was hoisted, the cruel deed was over
Gone was the man who loved Ireland so well
There was many a sad heart in Dublin that morning
When they murdered James Connolly, the Irish rebel

Many years have rolled by since the Irish Rebellion
When the guns of Brittania they loudly did speak
And the bold IRA they stood shoulder to shoulder
And the blood from their bodies flowed down Sackville Street

The Four Courts of Dublin the English bombarded
The spirit of freedom they tried hard to quell
But above all the din came the cry "No Surrender!"
'Twas the voice of James Connolly, the Irish rebel

The Rocky Road To Dublin

In Mullingar that night I rested limbs so weary
Started by daylight next morning bright and early
Took a drop o' the pure to keep me heart from sinking
That's an Irishman's cure when e'er he's on for drinking
See the lassies smile, laughing all the while
At my daring style, 'twould set your heart a-bubblin'
They asked if I was hired, wages I required
Till I was almost tired of the rocky road to Dublin. *Chorus*

In Dublin next arrived I thought it such a pity
To be so soon deprived a view of that fine city
When I took a stroll all among the quality
Me bundle it was stole in a neat locality

Something crossed me mind, then I looked behind
No bundle could I find on me stick a-wobblin'
Enquiring for the rogue, they said my Connaught brogue
Wasn't much in vogue on the rocky road to Dublin. *Chorus*

From there I got away, me spirits never failing
Landed on the quay as the ship was sailing
Captain at me roared, said that no room had he
When I jumped aboard, a cabin found for Paddy
Down among the pigs I played some funny rigs
Danced some hearty jigs, the water 'round me bubblin'
When off Holyhead I wished meself was dead
Or better far instead, on the rocky road to Dublin. *Chorus*

The boys of Liverpool when we safely landed
Called meself a fool, I could no longer stand it
Blood began to boil, temper I was losing
Poor old Erin's Isle they began abusing
"Hurrah, me boys!" says I, shillelagh I let fly
Some Galway boys were by and saw I was a-hobblin'
Then with loud "Hurray!" they joined in the affray
And quickly paved the way for the rocky road to Dublin. *Chorus*

~~~~~~~~~~~~~~~~

Avondale

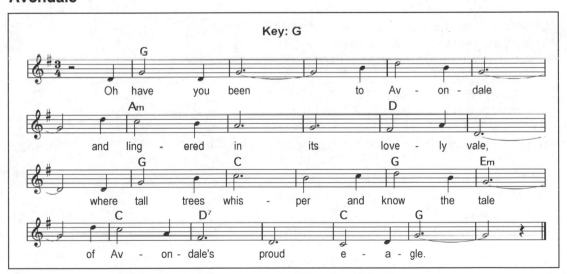

Where pride and ancient glory fade; so was the land where he was laid
Like Christ, was thirty pieces paid; for Avondale's proud eagle. *Chorus*

Long years that green and lovely vale; has nursed Parnell, her proudest Gael
And cursed the land that has betrayed; fair Avondale's proud eagle. *Chorus*

3

Courtin' In The Kitchen

Key: G

Come sin-gle belle and beau, un-to me pay at-ten-tion. Don't ev-er fall in love, 'tis the de-vil's own in-ven-tion. For once I fell in love with a maid-en so be-witch-in', Miss Hen-ri-et-ta Bell down in Cap-tain Kel-ly's kit-chen. **With me toor-a-loor-a-lay, me toor-a-loor-a-ladd-ie, sing too-ra-loo-ra-lay, toor-a-loor-a-ladd-ie.**

At the age of seventeen I was 'prenticed to a grocer
Not far from Stephen's Green where Miss Henri' used to go sir
Her manners were so fine; she set me heart a-twitchin'
When she asked meself to tea down in Captain Kelly's kitchen. *Chorus*

Now Sunday being the day when we were to have the flare-up
I dressed meself quite gay and I frizzed and oiled me hair up
The Captain had no wife and he'd gone off a-fishin'
So we kicked up the high life out of sight down in the kitchen. *Chorus*

Just as the clock struck six we sat down at the table
She handed tea and cakes and I ate what I was able
I had cakes with punch and tay till me side it got a stitch in
And the time it passed away with the courtin' in the kitchen. *Chorus*

With me arms around her waist she slyly hinted marriage
When through the door in haste we heard Captain Kelly's carriage
Her eyes told me full well, and they were not bewitchin'
That she wished I'd get to hell, or be somewhere from that kitchen. *Chorus*

4

She flew up off her knees, some five feet up or higher
And over head and heels threw me slap into the fire
My new Repealer's coat that I got from Mr. Mitchel
With a twenty shilling note went to blazes in the kitchen. *Chorus*

I grieved to see me duds all smeared with smoke and ashes
When a tub of dirty suds right into me face she dashes
As I lay on the floor and the water she kept pitchin'
Till a footman broke the door and came chargin' to the kitchen. *Chorus*

When the Captain came downstairs, though he seen me situation
Despite of all my prayers I was marched off to the station
For me they'd take no bail, though to get home I was itchin'
And I had to tell the tale of how I came into the kitchen. *Chorus*

I said she did invite me but she gave a flat denial
For assault she did indict me and meself was sent for trial
She swore I robbed the house in spite of all her screechin'
And I got six months hard for me courtin' in the kitchen. *Chorus*

~~~~~~~~~

The Harp That Once Through Tara's Halls

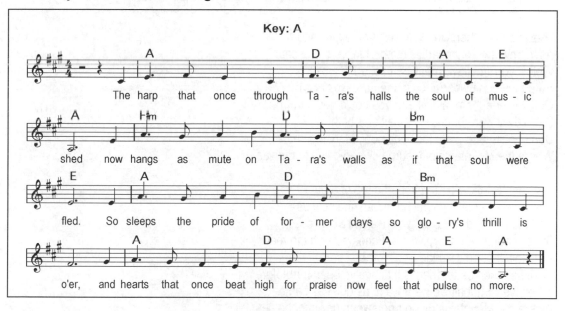

No more to chiefs and ladies bright the harp of Tara swells
The chord alone that breaks at night its tale of ruin tells
The freedom now so seldom wakes the only throb she gives
Is when some heart in sorrow breaks to show that still she lives

The Mountains Of Mourne

Key: G

(Lyrics under the music)

Oh Mar-y this Lon-don's a won-der-ful sight with the peop-le here work-ing by day and by night. They don't sow po-tat-oes nor bar-ley nor wheat, but there's gangs of them dig-ging for gold in the streets. At least when I asked them that's what I was told, so I just took a hand at this dig-ging for gold. But for all that I found there I might as well be where the Moun-tains of Mour-ne sweep down to the sea.

I believe that when writing a wish you expressed
As to how the young ladies of London were dressed
Well, if you'll believe me, when asked to a ball
Sure they don't wear a top to their dresses at all
Oh I've seen them myself and you could not in truth
Say if they were bound for a ball or a bath
Don't be starting them fashions now, Mary mo chroí*
Where the Mountains of Mourne sweep down to the sea

I've seen England's King from the top of a bus
Sure I never knew him but he means to know us
And though by the Saxon we once were oppressed
Still I cheered, God forgive me, I cheered with the rest
And now that he's visited Erin's green shore
We'll be much better friends than we've been heretofore
When we've got all we want we're as quiet as can be
Where the Mountains of Mourne sweep down to the sea

You remember young Peter O'Loughlin, of course
Well now he is here at the head of the Force
I met him today; I was crossing the Strand

And he stopped the whole street with one wave of his hand
And as we stood talking of days that were gone
The whole population of London looked on
But for all his great powers he's wishful like me
To be back where the dark Mourne sweeps down to the sea

There's beautiful girls here; oh never you mind
With beautiful shapes Nature never designed
And lovely complexions; all roses and cream
But O'Loughlin remarked with regard to the same
That if at those roses you venture to sip
The colour might all come away on your lip
So I'll wait for the wild rose that's waiting for me
Where the Mountains of Mourne sweep down to the sea

*Pronounced "cree" (my beloved)

~~~~~~~~~~~~~~

She Moved Through The Fair

She went away from me and she moved through the fair
And fondly I watched her move here and move there
And she made her way homeward with one star awake
As the swan in the evening moves over the lake

Last night I did dream that my love she came in
And so softly she came that her feet made no din
And she laid her hand on me and smiling did say
"It will not be long love, till our wedding day"

Bold Thady Quill

(The chorus is similar to the melody of the first four lines of the verse)

For rambling, for roving, for football or sporting, for emptying a bowl just as fast as you'd fill In all your days roving you'll find none so jovial as the Muskerry sportsman, the bold Thady Quill

Now Thady was famous in all sorts of places; at the athletic meeting held out in Cloughroe
He won the long jump without throwin' off his braces; goin' fifty-four feet, leppin' off from the toe
And at throwing the weight was a Dublinman foremost; but Thady outreached and exceed him still
And 'round the whole field went the wide ringing chorus; "Here's luck to our hero, the bold Thady Quill!"
Chorus

At the great hurling match between Cork and Tipp'rary; 'twas played in the Park by the banks of the Lee
Our own darling boys were afraid of being beaten; so they sent for bold Thady to Ballinagree
He hurled the ball left and right in their faces; and showed the Tipp'rary boys learning and skill
If they came in his way he was willing to brain them; the papers were full of the praise of Thade Quill
Chorus

In the year '91 before Parnell was taken; our Thade was outrageously breaking the peace
He got a light sentence for causing commotion; and six months hard labour for beating police
But in spite of coercion he's still agitating; ev'ry drop of his life's blood he's willing to spill
To gain for old Ireland complete liberation; till then there's no rest for the bold Thady Quill
Chorus

At the Cork Exhibition there was a fair lady; whose fortune exceeded a million or more
But a bad constitution had ruined her completely; and medical treatment had failed o'er and o'er
"Oh mother", she said, "sure I know what'll cure me; and all my diseases most certainly kill
Give over your doctors and medical treatment; I'd rather one squeeze from the bold Thady Quill!"
Chorus

~~~~~~~~~~~~~~

The Hills Of Kerry
(Verses and chorus have the same melody)

The noble and the brave have departed from our shore
They've gone off to a foreign land where the mighty canyons roar
No more they'll see the shamrock or the hills so dear to me
Or hear the small birds singing all around you, sweet Tralee. *Chorus*

No more the sun will shine on that blessed harvest morn
Or hear the reaper singing in the fields of golden corn
There's a balm for every woe and a cure for every pain
But the pretty smile of my darling girl I will never see again. *Chorus*

9

Paddy Lay Back

Now some of our fellows had been drinking; and me meself was heavy on the booze
So I sat upon me old sea chest a-thinking; I'll just turn in and have meself a snooze
Well I wished that I was in the Jolly Sailors; along with Irish Paddys drinking beer
Then I thought of what a jolly lot are sailors; and with me flipper I wiped away a tear
Chorus

Well when we gathered all the tugs alongside; they towed us from the wharf and out to sea
With half the crew a hanging o'er the ship's side; the bloody row that started sickened me
The bowsen he said that he couldn't savvy; the crew were speaking lingoes all galore
So the only thing the old man he could do was; just pay us sailors off and ship some more
Chorus

The Rose Of Tralee

The cool shades of evening their mantles were spreading
And Mary, all smiling, sat list'ning to me
The moon through the valley her pale rays was shedding
When I won the heart of the Rose of Tralee. *Chorus*

The Bonny Boy

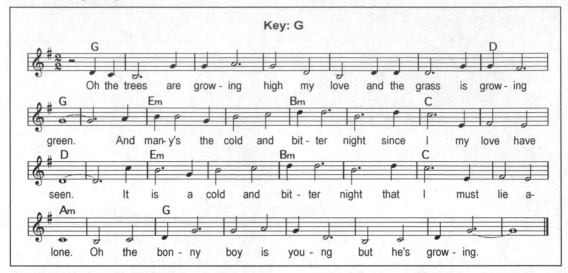

Oh the trees are grow-ing high my love and the grass is grow-ing green. And man-y's the cold and bit-ter night since I my love have seen. It is a cold and bit-ter night that I must lie a-lone. Oh the bon-ny boy is you-ng but he's grow-ing.

Oh Father dear father I think you did me wrong
For to go and get me married to one who is so young
For he is only sixteen years and I am twenty-one
And the bonny boy is young and still growing

Oh daughter dear daughter I did not do you wrong
For to go and get you married to one who is so young
He will be a match for you when I am dead and gone
Oh the bonny boy is young but he's growing

Oh Father dear father I'll tell you what I'll do
I'll send my love to college for another year or two
And all around his college cap I'll tie a ribbon blue
Just to show the other girls that he's married

At evening when strolling down by the college wall
You'd see the young collegiates a-playing at the ball
You'd see him in amongst them there, the fairest of them all
He's my bonny boy, he's young but he's growing

At the early age of sixteen years he was a married man
And at the age of seventeen the father of a son
But at the age of eighteen o'er his grave the grass grew strong
Cruel death put an end to his growing

I will make my love a shroud of the highest Holland brown
And whilst I am a-weaving it my tears they will flow down
For once I had a true love but now he's lying low
And I'll nurse his bonny boy while he's growing

~~~~~~~~~~~~~~

The Curragh Of Kildare

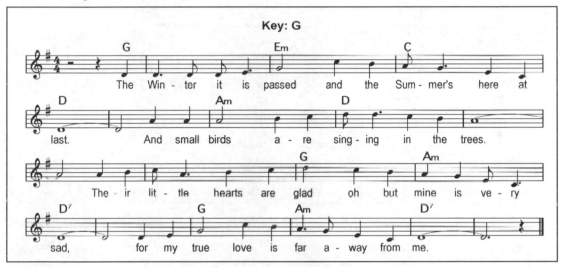

Key: G

The Win - ter it is passed and the Sum - mer's here at last. And small birds a - re sing - ing in the trees. The - ir lit - tle hearts are glad oh but mine is ve - ry sad, for my true love is far a - way from me.

All you that are in love and cannot it remove; I pity all the pain that you endure
For experience lets me know that your hearts are full of woe; it's a woe that no mortal can endure

A livery I will wear and I'll straighten back my hair; in velvet so green I will appear
And it's then I will repair to the Curragh of Kildare; for it's there I'll find tidings of my dear

The rose upon the briar and the water running free; gives joy to the linnet and the bee
Their little hearts are blessed but mine is not at rest; for my true love is absent from me

And it's then I will repair to the Curragh of Kildare; for it's there I'll find tidings of my dear

Lanigan's Ball

Meself to be sure got free invitations for all the nice colleens and boys I might ask
Just in a minute both friends and relations were dancing as merry as bees 'round a cask
There was lashings of punch, wine for the ladies; potatoes and cakes, there was bacon and tay
There were the Nolans, the Dolans, O'Gradys courting the girls and dancing away

They were doing all kinds of nonsensical polkas all 'round the room in a whirligig
Till Julie and I soon banished their nonsense and tipped them a twist of a real Irish jig
O how that girl she got mad and we danced till we thought that the ceilings would fall
For I spent three weeks at Brook's Academy learning to dance for Lanigan's Ball. *Chorus*

The boys were all merry, the girls all hearty dancing together in couples and groups
Till an accident happened, young Terence McCarthy; he put his right leg through Miss Finnerty's hoops
The creature she fainted and called "melia merder"; called for her brothers and gathered them all
Carmody swore that he'd go no further; he'd get satisfaction at Lanigan's Ball

In the midst of the row Miss Kerrigan fainted; her cheeks at the same time as red as a rose
Some of the boys decreed she was painted; she took a small drop too much I suppose
Her sweetheart Ned Morgan so powerful and able; when he saw his fair colleen stretched by the wall
He tore the left leg from under the table and smashed all the dishes at Lanigan's Ball. *Chorus*

Boys, O boys 'tis then there was ructions; I took a leg from young Phelim McHugh
But soon I replied to his fine introductions and kicked him a terrible hullabaloo
Old Casey the piper he nearly got strangled; they squeezed up his pipes, bellows, chanters and all
The girls in their ribbons they all got entangled and that put an end to Lanigan's Ball. *Chorus*

Red Is The Rose
(Verses and chorus have the same melody)

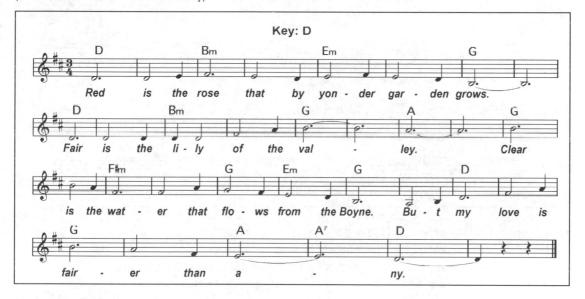

'Twas down by Killarney's green woodlands that we strayed
The moon and the stars they were shining
The moon shone its rays on her locks of golden hair
She swore she'd be my love forever. *Chorus*

It's not for the parting that my sister pains
It's not for the grief of my mother
It's all for the loss of my bonnie Irish lass
That my heart is breaking forever. *Chorus*

Finnegan's Wake

Key: C

Tim Finn- eg- an lived in Wat- ling Street, a gen- tle- man Ir- ish

might- y odd. He had a brogue both rich and sweet, and to

rise in the world he carr- ied a hod. Tim had a bit of a

tip- pl- in' way. With the love of the liq- uor he was born. And to

send him on his way each day a drop of the creath- ur*

ev- ery morn. *Whack fol - de - da, will you dance with your part- ner a-*

round the floor your trot - ters shake. Is - n't it the

truth I told ye, lots of fun at Finn - eg - an's wake!

One morning Tim was rather full; his head felt heavy which made him shake
He fell off the ladder and he broke his skull and they carried him home his corpse to wake
And they wrapped him up in a nice clean sheet and they laid him out upon the bed
With a bottle of whiskey at his feet and a barrel of porter at his head. **Chorus**

His friends assembled at the wake and Mrs. Finnegan called for lunch
First she gave them tay and cake, then piped tobacco and brandy punch
Then the Widow Malone began to cry; such a lovely corpse she did ever see
"Yerra Tim mo bhourneen** why did you die"; "Will you hold your hour" said Molly Magee. *Chorus*

Then Mary Murphy took up the job; "Yerra Biddy" says she "You're wrong, I'm sure"
Then Biddy fetched her a belt in the gob and left her sprawling on the floor
Civil war did then engage; woman to woman and man to man
Shillelagh law was all the rage and a row and a ruction soon began. *Chorus*

Tim Moloney ducked his head when a bottle of whiskey flew at him
He ducked and, landing on the bed, the whiskey scattered over Tim
Well begob he revives and see how he's rising; Tim Finnegan rising in the bed
Saying "Fling your whiskey 'round like blazes! Be the thundering Jayses d'ye think I'm dead!" *Chorus*

*Booze – usually whiskey
** Pronounced "mo vourneen' (my loved one)

~~~~~~~~~~~~~~~

My Singing Bird

Key: G

I-'ve seen the lark so-ar high at morn to si-ng u-p in the blue.

I-'ve heard the black-bi-rd pipe his song, the thr-ush and the lin-net too.

Bu-t none of them can sing so sweet, my sing-ing bi-rd a-s you.

Ah ah ah ah ah ah ah ah ah ah, m-y si-ng-i-ng bird as you.

If I could lure my singing bird down from its own cosy nest
If I could catch my singing bird I'd warm it upon my breast
And in my heart my singing bird would sing itself to rest
Ah, etc. would sing itself to rest

Whiskey In The Jar

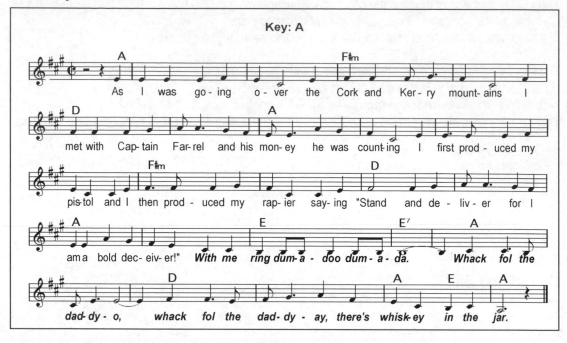

I counted out his money and it made a pretty penny
I put it in my pocket and I brought it home to Jenny
She sighed and she vowed that she never would deceive me
But the devil take the women for they never can be easy. *Chorus*

I went into her chamber all for to take a slumber
I dreamt of gold and jewels and for sure it was no wonder
But Jenny took my pistols and she filled them full of water
And sent for Captain Farrell to be ready for the slaughter. *Chorus*

'Twas early in the morning just before I rose to travel
The redcoats stood around the bed and likewise Captain Farrell
I then produced my pistols for she stole away my rapier
I couldn't shoot with water so a prisoner I was taken. *Chorus*

They threw me into prison, bound without a writ or bounty
For robbin' Captain Farrell near the Cork and Kerry mountains
But they couldn't take me fist so I punched and knocked the sentry
And bade no farewell to the Captain or the gentry. *Chorus*

If I could find my brother who is listed in the army
I know that he would rescue me in Cork or in Killarney
We'd set out from this place and go roving in Kilkenny
I'd be much safer there than beside my faithless Jenny. *Chorus*

Some men delight in fishing, others they like bowling
Some men like the fields or the sea that goes a-rolling
But me I take my pleasures in the juice of the barley
And not courting pretty maidens in the morning bright and early. *Chorus*

~~~~~~~~~~~~

A Bunch Of Thyme

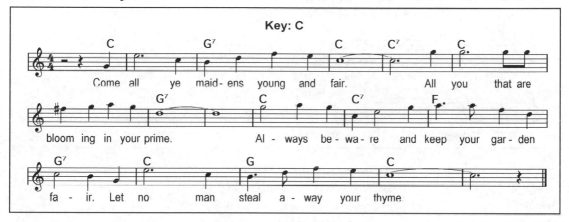

For thyme, it is a precious thing; and thyme brings all things to my mind
Thyme with all its flavours, along with all its joys; thyme brings all things to my mind

Once I had a bunch of thyme; I thought it never would decay
Then came a lusty sailor who chanced to pass my way; he stole my bunch of thyme away

The sailor gave to me a rose; a rose that never would decay
He gave it to me, to keep me reminded; of when he stole my thyme away

(Repeat first verse)

The Rising Of The Moon

Key: D

"Oh then tell me, Sean O' Farr-ell, tell me why you hur-ry so". "Hush a

bhuach-aill* hush and list-en!", and his cheeks were all a-glow. "I bear or-ders from the

Cap-tain, get you read-y quick and soon, for the pikes must be to-geth-er at the

ris-ing of the moon!". At the ris-ing of the mo-on, at the ris-ing of the

moon. For the pikes must be to-geth-er at the ris-ing of the moon.

"Oh then tell me Sean O'Farrell where the gathering's to be"
"In the old spot by the river, right well known to you and me
One word more - for signal token, whistle up the marching tune
With your pike upon your shoulder by the rising of the moon"
By the rising of the moon, by the rising of the moon
With your pike upon your shoulder by the rising of the moon

Out of many a mud-wall cabin eyes were watching out that night
Many a manly heart was throbbing for that blessed warning light
Murmurs passed along the valley like a banshee's lonely croon
And a thousand blades were flashing at the rising of the moon
At the rising of the moon, at the rising of the moon
And a thousand blades were flashing at the rising of the moon

There beside that singing river that dark mass of men was seen
Far above the shining weapons hung their own beloved green
"Death to every foe and traitor! Forward! Strike the marching tune
And hurrah, me boys, for freedom! 'Tis the rising of the moon"
'Tis the rising of the moon, 'tis the rising of the moon
And hurrah, me boys, for freedom 'tis the rising of the moon

Well they fought for dear old Ireland and full bitter was their fate
(Oh what glorious pride and sorrow fills the name of "Ninety-Eight")
Yet thank God e'en still are beating hearts in manhood's burning noon
Who would follow in their footsteps at the rising of the moon
At the rising of the moon, at the rising of the moon
Who would follow in their footsteps at the rising of the moon

*Pronounced "voukill" (boy)

Let The Grasses Grow

Key: G

Let the grass-es grow and the wat-ers flow in a free and eas-y way, but give me en-ough of the rare old stuff that's made near Gal-way Bay. And po-lice-men all from Do-ne-gal, Sli-go and Leit-rim too. We'll give them the slip and we'll take a sip of the rare old moun-tain dew.

At the foot of the hill there's a neat little still where the smoke curls up to the sky
By a whiff of a smell you can plainly tell there's a poitin still nearby
Oh it fills the air with a perfume rare and betwixt both me and you
As home we roll we can drink a bowl or a bucket of mountain dew. *Chorus*

Now learned men who use the pen have wrote the praises high
Of the sweet poitin from Ireland green distilled from wheat and rye
Away with pills, it'll cure all ills of Pagan, Christian or Jew
So take off your coat and grease your throat with the real old mountain dew. *Chorus*

O'Donnell Abú

Princely O'Neill to our aid is advancing
With many a chieftain and warrior clan
A thousand proud steeds in his vanguard are prancing
'Neath the borderers brave from the banks of the Bann
Many a heart shall quail under its coat of mail
Deeply the merciless foeman shall rue
When on his ear shall ring, borne on the breeze's wing
Tir Connell's dread war cry "O'Donnell Abú!"

Wildly o'er Desmond the war-wolf is howling
Fearless the eagle sweeps over the plain
The fox in the streets of the city is prowling
And all who would scare them are banished or slain
Grasp, every stalwart hand, hackbut and battle-brand
Pay them all back the deep debt so long due
Norris and Clifford well can of Tir Connell tell
Onward to glory, O'Donnell Abú!

Sacred the cause that Clan Connell's defending
The alters we kneel at, the homes of our sires
Ruthless the ruin the foe is extending
Midnight is red with the plunderer's fires
On with O'Donnell then, fight the old fight again
Sons of Tir Connell all valiant and true
Make the false Saxon feel Erin's avenging steel
Strike for your country, O'Donnell Abú!

The Last Rose Of Summer

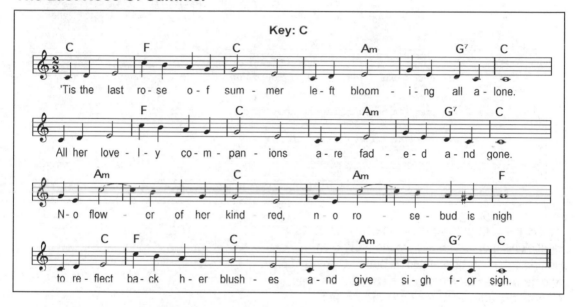

I'll not leave thee, thou alone one, to pine on the stem
Since the lovely are sleeping go sleep, thou, with them
Thus kindly I scatter they leaves o'er the bed
Where thy mates of the garden lie scentless and dead

So soon may I follow when friendships decay
And from love's shining circle the gems drop away
When true hearts lie withered and fond ones are flown
Oh who would inhabit this bleak world alone!

Monto

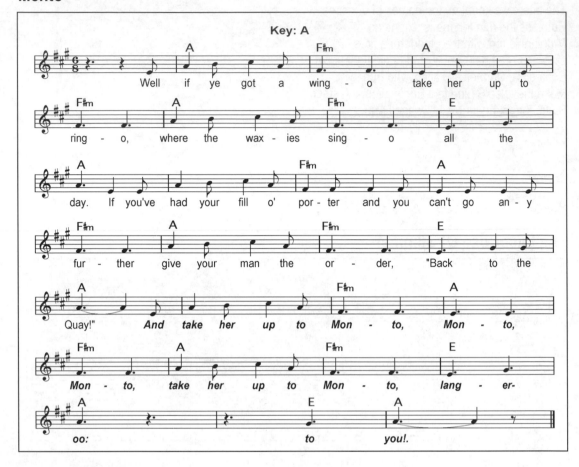

You've heard of Butcher Foster the dirty old impostor
He took his mot and lost her up the Furry Glen
He first put on his bowler and he buttoned up his trousers
And he whistled for a growler and he said "My man
Chorus change: Take me up to Monto, etc.

You've heard the Dublin Fusiliers, the dirty old bamboozileers
They went and got their childer, one, two, three
They march them from the Linen Hall; there's one for every cannon ball
And Vicky's going to send them all o'er the sea
Chorus change: But they'll first go up to Monto, etc.

When Carey told on Skin-the-Goat, O'Donnell caught him on the boat
He wished he'd never been afloat, the dirty skite
It wasn't very sensible to tell on the Invincibles
They stuck up for the principles, day and night
Chorus change: By going up to Monto, etc.

When the Czar o' Roosha and the King o' Proosha
Landed in the Phoenix in a big balloon
They asked the Garda Band to play 'The Wearing of the Green'
But the buggers in the depot didn't know the tune
Chorus change: So they took them up to Monto, etc.

The Queen she came to call on us; she wanted to see all of us
I'm glad she didn't fall on us; she's eighteen stone
"Mister Mayor, melord", says she, "is that all you've got to show to me"
"Why no ma'am there's some more to see - póg mo thóin!"*
Chorus change: And he took her up to Monto, etc.

Pronounced "Poag mo hoan". (Kiss my a - - e!)
~~~~~~~~~~~~~~

When You Were Sweet Sixteen

Key: G

When first I saw the love light in your eyes, I thought the world held nought but joy for me. And ev-en though we drif-ted far a part I nev-er dream but what I dream of thee. I love you as I never loved be-fore, since first I met you on the vil-lage green. Come to me e'er my dreamof love is o'er. I love you as I loved you when you were sweet, when you were sweet six-teen.

Last night I dreamt I held your hand in mine; and once again you were my happy bride
I kissed you as I did in 'Auld Lang Syne'; as to the church we wandered side by side
Chorus

25

The Galway Races

There were passengers from Limerick town and more from Tipperary
Boys from Connemara and a flair of married ladies
People from Cork City who were loyal, true and faithful
Who brought home the Fenian prisoners from dying in foreign nations. *Chorus*

It's there you'll see the pipers and the fiddlers competing
The nimble-footed dancers a-trippin' o'er the daisies
There were others crying "Cigars and lights and bills for all the races"
With the colours of the jockeys and the price and horses' ages. *Chorus*

It's there you'll see confectioners with sugar sticks and dainties
The lozenges and oranges, the lemonade and raisins
The gingerbread and spices to accommodate the ladies
And a big crubeen for threepence to be picking while you're able. *Chorus*

It's there you'll see the jockeys and they're mounted up so stately
The pink, the blue, the orange and green, the emblems of our nation
When the bell was rung for starting all the horses seemed impatient
I thought they never stood on ground their speed was so amazing. *Chorus*

There were half a million people there from all denominations
The Catholic, the Protestant, the Jew and Presbyterian
There was yet no animosity no matter what persuasion
But sportsmen's hospitality to induce fresh acquaintance. *(Repeat chorus twice)*

I Know Where I'm Going

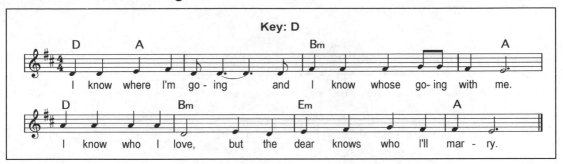

Some will say he's dark, some will say he's bonny
But the fairest of them all is my handsome noble Johnny

I have stockings of silk, shoes of fine green leather
Combs to bind my hair and a ring for every finger

Feather beds are soft and painted rooms are bonny
But I would leave them all to be with my darling Johnny

(Repeat first verse)

The Foggy Dew

Right proudly high in Dublin town they hoisted up the flag of war
'Twas better to die 'neath an Irish sky that at Suvle or Sud el Bar
And from the plains of Royal Meath strong men came hurrying through
While Brittania's Huns with their great big guns sailed in through the foggy dew

Oh the night fell black and the rifles' crack made "Perfidious Albion" reel
'Mid the leaden rain seven tongues of flame did shine o'er the lines of steel
By each shining blade a prayer was said that to Ireland her sons be true
When the morning broke still the war flag shook out its folds in the foggy dew

'Twas England bade our Wild Geese go so that small nations might be free
But their lonely graves are by Suvla's waves or the fringe of the Great North Sea
Oh had they died by Pearse'e side or had fought with Cathal Brugha
Their names we'd keep where the Fenians sleep 'neath the shroud of the foggy dew

But the bravest fell and the requiem bell rang out mournfully and clear
For those who died that water tide in the springtime of the year
While the world did gaze with deep amaze at those fearless men, but few
Who bore the fight that Freedom's light might shine through the foggy dew

Ah! back through the glen I rode again and my heart with grief was sore
For I parted then with valiant men whom I never will see no more
But to and fro in my dreams I go and I'd kneel and pray for you
For slavery fled, O glorious dead, when you fell in the foggy dew

The Minstrel Boy

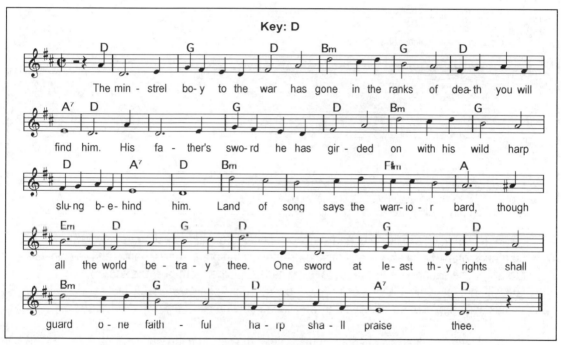

The Minstrel fell but the foeman's chain could not bring his proud soul under
The harp he loved never spoke again; for he tore its chords asunder
And said "No chains shall sully thee; thou soul of love and bravery
Thy songs were made for the pure and free; they shall never sound in slavery"

The Banks Of My Own Lovely Lee

And then in the springtime of laughter and song; can I ever forget the sweet hours
With the friends of my youth as we rambled along; 'mongst the green mossy banks and wild flowers
Then too, when the evening's sun sinking to rest; sheds its golden light over the sea
The maid with her lover the wild daisies pressed; on the banks of my own lovely Lee
Yes the maid with her lover wild daisies they pressed; on the banks of my own lovely Lee

'Tis a beautiful land this dear isle of song; its gems shed their light on the world
And her faithful sons bore thro' ages of wrong; the banner St. Patrick unfurled
Oh, would I were there with the friends I love best; and my fond bosom partner with me
We'd roam thy bank over and when weary we'd rest; by thy waters, my own lovely Lee
Yes we'd roam thy banks over and when weary we'd rest; by thy waters, my own lovely Lee

Oh what joys should be mine e're this life should decline; to seek shells on thy sea-gilded shore
While the steel-feathered eagle, oft splashing the brine; brings longing for freedom once more
Oh all that upon earth I wish for or crave; that my last crimson drop be for thee
To moisten the grass on my forefathers' grave; on the banks of my own lovely Lee
Yes to moisten the grass on my forefathers' grave; on the banks of my own lovely Lee

Bunclody

The streams of Bunclody they flow down so free; by the streams of Bunclody I'm longing to be
A-drinking strong liquor in the height of my cheer; here's a health to Bunclody and the lass I love dear

Oh, 'tis why my love slights me as you might understand; for she has a freehold and I have no land
She has great stores of riches and a fine sum of gold; and everything fitting a house to uphold

If I were a clerk and could write a good hand; I would write my love a letter that she would understand
For I am a young fellow that is wounded in love; once I lived in Bunclody but now I must remove

So fare thee well father and mother, adieu; my sisters and brothers farewell unto you
I am bound for Americay my fortune to try; when I think of Bunclody I'm ready to die

Brennan On The Moor

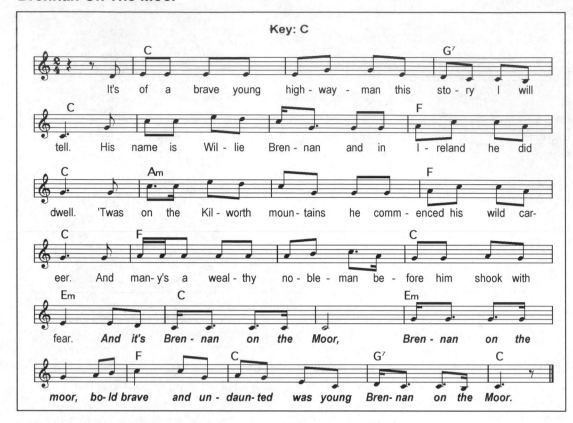

Key: C

It's of a brave young high-way-man this sto-ry I will tell. His name is Wil-lie Bren-nan and in I-reland he did dwell. 'Twas on the Kil-worth moun-tains he comm-enced his wild car-eer. And man-y's a weal-thy no-ble-man be-fore him shook with fear. *And it's Bren-nan on the Moor, Bren-nan on the moor, bo-ld brave and un-daun-ted was young Bren-nan on the Moor.*

One day upon the highway as Willie he went down
He met the Mayor of Cashel a mile outside the town
The mayor he knew his features and he said "Young man" said he
"Your name is Willie Brennan you must come along with me"
Chorus - And it's Brennan on the Moore, etc.

Now Brennan's wife had gone to town, provisions for to buy
And when she saw her Willie she began to weep and cry
She said "Hand me that tenpenny" as soon as Willie spoke
She handed him a blunderbus from underneath her cloak
Chorus - For young Brennan on the Moore, etc.

Then with his loaded blunderbus the truth I will unfold
He made the mayor to tremble and robbed him of his gold
One hundred pounds was offered for his apprehension there
So he with horse and saddle to the mountains did repair
Chorus - Did young Brennan on the Moore, etc.

Now Brennan being an outlaw and upon the mountain high
With cavalry and infantry to take him they did try
He laughed at them with scorn until at last as it was said
By a false-hearted woman he was cruelly betrayed
Chorus - Was young Brennan on the Moor, etc.

~~~~~~~~~~~~~

Botany Bay

(Verses and chorus have the same melody)

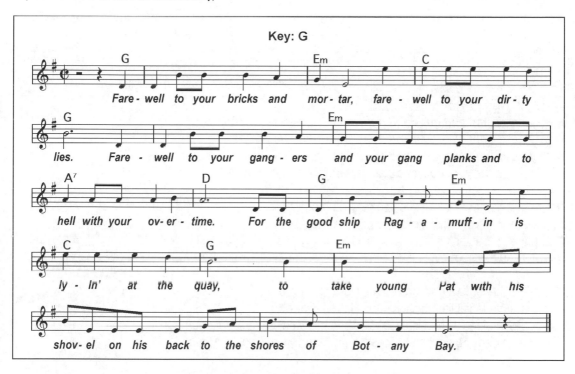

The boss came up this morning, he says "Well Pat you know
If you don't get your navvys out I'm afraid you'll have to go"
So I asked him for my wages and demanded all my pay
For I told him straight I will emigrate to the shores of Botany Bay. *Chorus*

And when I reach Australia I'll go and search for gold
There's plenty there for digging or so I have been told
Or else I'll go back to my trade and a hundred bricks I'll lay
Because I live for an eight hour shift on the shores of Botany Bay. *Chorus*

Johnny I Hardly Knew Ye
(Versus and chorus have the same melody)

While go-ing the road to sweet A - thy, har - oo, har - oo. While
go-ing the road to sweet A - thy, har - oo, har - oo. While
go-ing the road to sweet A - thy, a stick in me hand and a tear in me eye, a
dole-ful dam-sel I heard cry, "John-ny, I hard-ly knew ye".

With your drums and guns and guns and drums Ha-roo, Ha-roo
With your drums and guns and guns and drums Ha-roo, Ha-roo
With your drums and guns and guns and drums the enemy nearly slew ye
My darling dear you look so queer, Johnny I hardly knew ye!

Where are your eyes that looked so mild Ha-roo, Ha-roo
Where are your eyes that looked so mild Ha-roo, Ha-roo
Where are your eyes that looked so mild when my poor heart you first beguiled
Why did you run from me and the child, Johnny I hardly knew ye. *Chorus*

Where are the legs with which you run Ha-roo, Ha-roo
Where are the legs with which you run Ha-roo, Ha-roo
Where are the legs with which you run when you went off to carry a gun
Indeed your dancing days are done, Johnny I hardly knew ye. *Chorus*

It grieved my heart to see you sail Ha-roo, Ha-roo
It grieved my heart to see you sail Ha-roo, Ha-roo
It grieved my heart to see you sail though from my heart you took leg-bail
Like a cod you're doubled up head and tail, Johnny I hardly knew ye. *Chorus*

You haven't an arm you haven't a leg Ha-roo, Ha-roo
You haven't an arm you haven't a leg Ha-roo, Ha-roo
You haven't an arm you haven't a leg you're an eyeless, noseless, chickenless egg
You'll have to be put in a bowl to beg, Johnny I hardly knew ye. *Chorus*

I'm happy for to see you home Ha-roo, Ha-roo
I'm happy for to see you home Ha-roo, Ha-roo
I'm happy for to see you home all from the island of Sulloon*
So low in flesh so high in bone, Johnny I hardly knew you. *Chorus*

But sad as it is to see you so Ha-roo, Ha-roo
But sad as it is to see you so Ha-roo, Ha-roo
But sad as it is to see you so I think of you now as an object of woe
Your Peggy'll still keep you on as her beau, Johnny I hardly knew ye. *Chorus*

*Ceylon

~~~~~~~~~~~~~

The Merry Ploughboy
(Verses and chorus have the same melody)

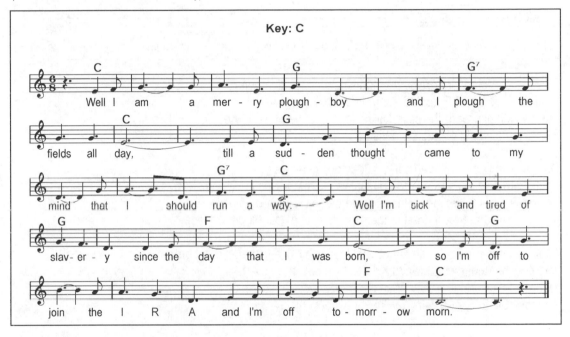

So I'm off to Dublin in the green, in the green; where the helmets glisten in the sun
Where the bayonets flash and the rifles crash; to the echo of a Thompson gun

I'll leave aside my pick and spade, I'll leave aside my plough
I'll leave aside my old grey mare for no more I'll need them now. *Chorus*

And I'll leave aside my Mary, she's the girl that I adore
And I wonder if she'll think of me when she hears the cannons roar
And when the war is over, and dear old Ireland's free
I will take her to the church to wed and a rebel's wife she'll be. *Chorus*

The Scariff Martyrs

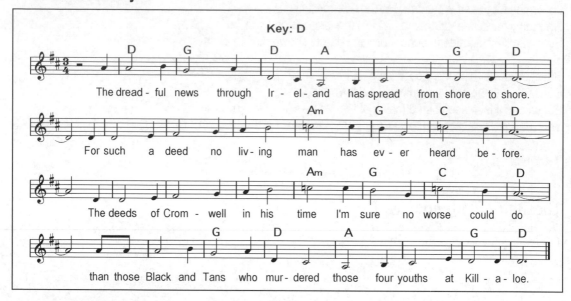

Key: D

The dread-ful news through Ir-el-and has spread from shore to shore.
For such a deed no liv-ing man has ev-er heard be-fore.
The deeds of Crom-well in his time I'm sure no worse could do
than those Black and Tans who mur-dered those four youths at Kill-a-loe.

Three of the four were on the run and searched for all around
Until with this brave Egan lad from Williamstown was found
They asked him were the boys inside; in honour he proved true
Because he would not tell the pass he was shot in Killaloe

On the fourth day of November, that day of sad renown
They were sold and traced through Galway to that house in Williamstown
They never got a fighting chance but were captured while asleep
And the way that they ill-treated them would cause your blood to creep

They bound them tight both hands and feet with twine they could not break
And they brought them down to Killaloe by steamer on the lake
Without clergy, judge or jury upon the bridge they shot them down
And their blood flowed with the Shannon, convenient to the town

With three days of perseverance, their bodies they let go
At ten o'clock at night their funeral passed through Ogonolloe
They were kept in Scariff chapel for two nights and a day
Now in that place of rest they lie; kind people for them pray

If you were at their funeral, it was an awful sight
To see the local clergy and they all dressed up in white
Such a sight as these four martyrs in one grave was never seen
For they died to save the flag they loved, the orange white and green

Now that they are dead and gone I hope in peace they'll rest
Like all their Irish brave comrades, forever among the blessed
The day will come when all will know who sold the lives away
Of young McMahon, Rogers, valiant Egan and Kildea

~~~~~~~~~~~~~

The Bold O'Donoghue

(Verses and chorus have the same melody)

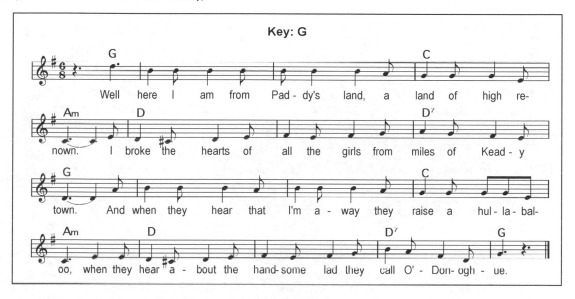

For I'm the boy to please her and I'm the boy to tease her
I'm the boy to squeeze her and I'll tell you what I'll do
I'll court her like an Irishman with me brogue and blarney too
With me rollikin, swollikin, dollikin, wollikin bold O'Donoghue

I wish me love was a red red rose growing on yonder wall
And me to be a dewdrop and upon her brow I'd fall
Perhaps now she might think of me as a rather heavy dew
No more she'd love the handsome lad they call O'Donoghue. *Chorus*

They say that Queen Victoria has a daughter fine and grand
Perhaps she'd take it into her head for to marry an Irishman
And if I could only get a chance to have a word or two
Perhaps she'd take a notion in the Bold O'Donoghue! *Chorus*

Fiddlers Green

Now Fiddlers Green is a place I hear tell
Where fishermen go if they don't go to hell
Where the skies are all clear and the dolphins do play
And the cold coast of Greenland is far far away. *Chorus*

When you get to the docks and the long trip is through
And there's pubs and there's clubs and there's lassies there too
Where the girls are all pretty and the beer it is free
And there's bottles of rum growing from every tree. *Chorus*

Now I don't want a harp nor a halo, not me
Just give me a breeze and a good rolling sea
I'll play me old squeezebox as we sail along
With the wind in the rigging to sing me a song. *Chorus*

The Wild Rover

I went into an alehouse I used to frequent
I told the landlady my money was spent
I asked her for credit, she answered me "Nay
Such custom as yours I can have any day". *Chorus*

I took out from my pocket ten sovereigns bright
And the landlady's eyes opened wide with delight
She said "I've got whiskeys and wines of the best
And the words that I spoke they were only in jest". *Chorus*

I'll go home to my parents, confess what I've done
And I'll ask them to pardon their prodigal son
And if they caress me as oft times before
Sure I never will play the wild rover no more. *Chorus*

Spancil Hill

Delighted by the novelty; enchanted with the scene
Where in my early boyhood where often I had been
I thought I heard a murmur and I think I hear it still
It's the little stream of water that flows down by Spancil Hill

To amuse a passing fancy I lay down on the ground
And all my school companions were shortly gathered around
When we were home returning we would dance with bright goodwill
To Martin Moynihan's music at the cross at Spancil Hill

It was on the twenty-third of June; the day before the fair
When Ireland's sons and daughters and friends assembled there
The young, the old, the brave and the bold, their duty to fulfil
At the parish church at Clooney, just a mile from Spancil Hill

I went to see my neighbours and to hear what they might say
The old ones were all dead and gone; the young ones gone away
I met the tailor Quigley; he's as bold as ever still
Sure he used to mend my britches when I lived at Spancil Hill

I paid a flying visit to my first and only love
She's as fair as any lily and as gentle as a dove
She threw her arms around me sayin' "Johnny I love you still"
For she was a farmer's daughter and the pride of Spancil Hill

Well I dreamt I hugged and kissed her, as in the days of yore
She said "Johnny, you're only joking!"; as many's the time before
The cock she crew in the morning; she crew both loud and shrill
And I awoke in California, many miles from Spancil Hill

~~~~~~~~~~~~~~~

Boston Burglar

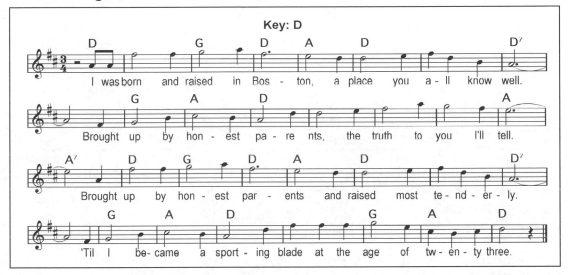

My character was taken and I was sent to jail
My parents tried to bail me out but found it all in vain
The jury found me guilty the clerk he wrote it down
The judge he passed my sentence, to be sent to Charlestown

I see my aged father and he standing by the Bar
Likewise my aged mother and she tearing at her hair
The tearing of her old grey locks and the tears came mingled down
Saying "John my son, what have you done that you're bound for Charlestown?"

There is a girl in Boston, a place you all know well
And if e'er I get my liberty it's with her I will dwell
If e'er I get my liberty bad company I will shun
The robbing of the National Bank and the drinking of the rum

You lads that are at liberty should keep it while you can
Don't roam the streets by night or day or break the laws of man
For if you do you're sure to rue and become a lad like me
A-serving up your youthful years in the Royal Artillery

Skibbereen

Oh son, I loved my native land with energy and pride
Until a blight came o'er my crops; my sheep and cattle died
My rent and taxes were so high I could not them redeem
And that's the cruel reason why I left old Skibbereen

It is so well I do recall that bleak December day
The landlord and the sheriff came to drive us all away
They set my roof on fire with their cursed English spleen
And that's another reason why I left old Skibbereen

Your mother too, God rest her soul, fell on the snowy ground
Her treasured life's possessions they lay trampled all around
She never rose but passed away, from life to mortal dream
And found a quiet resting place in dear old Skibbereen

And you were only two years old and feeble was your frame
I could not leave you with my friends; you bore your father's name
I wrapped you in a blanket at the dead of night unseen
I heaved a sigh and bade goodbye to dear old Skibbereen

Oh father dear the day will come when vengeance loud will call
All Irishmen with stern of faith will rally one and all
I'll be the man to lead the van beneath the flag of green
And loud and high we'll raise the cry "Remember Skibbereen!"

Dicey Reilly

(Verses and chorus have the same melody)

She walks along Fitzgibbon Street with an independent air
And then it's down by Summerhill where the people stop and stare
She says "It's nearly half past one, it's time I had another little one"
Ah the heart of the rowl is Dicey Reilly. *Chorus*

She owns a little sweet shop at the corner of the street
And every evening after school I go to wash her feet
She leaves me there to mind the shop while she nips in for another little drop
Ah the heart of the rowl is Dicey Reilly. *Chorus*

*Old

The Juice Of The Barley

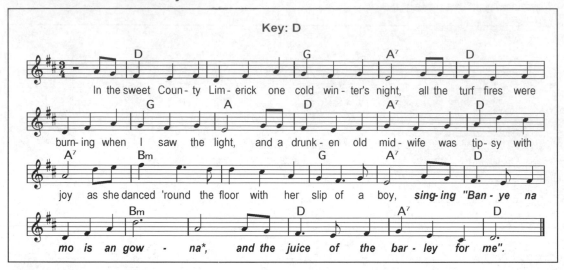

Key: D

In the sweet Coun-ty Lim-erick one cold win-ter's night, all the turf fires were burn-ing when I saw the light, and a drunk-en old mid-wife was tip-sy with joy as she danced 'round the floor with her slip of a boy, *sing-ing "Ban-ye na mo is an gow - na*, and the juice of the bar-ley for me".*

Well when I was a gassoon** of eight years or so
With me turf and me primer to school I did go
To a dusty old schoolhouse without any door
Where lay the schoolmaster blind drunk on the floor. *Chorus*

At the learning I wasn't such a genius I'm thinking
But I soon bet the master entirely at drinking
Not a wake nor a wedding for five miles around
But meself in the corner was sure to be found. *Chorus*

One Sunday the priest read me out from the alter
Saying "You'll end up your days with your neck in a halter
And you'll dance a fine jig betwixt heaven and hell"
And the words they did frighten, the truth for to tell. *Chorus*

So the very next morning as the dawn it did break
I went down to the vestry the pledge for to take
And there in that room sat the priests in a bunch
'Round a big roaring fire drinking tumblers of punch. *Chorus*

Well from that day to this I have wandered alone
I'm a Jack of all Trades and a master of none
With the sky for me roof and the earth for me floor
And I'll dance out me days drinking whiskey galore. *Chorus*

*Pronounced "Ban-ya na mo iss an gow-na" (The milk of the cows and the calf)
** Young lad.

44

I'll Tell Me Ma

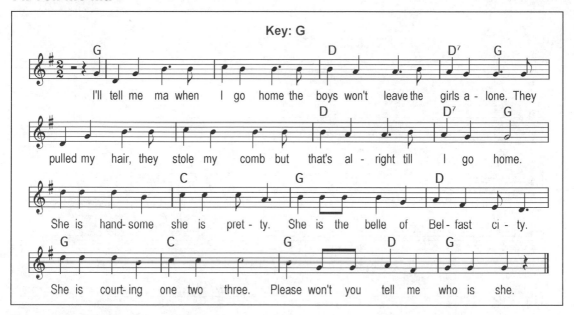

Albert Mooney says he loves her; all the boys are fighting for her
They rap at the door and they ring at the bell saying "O my true love are you well"
Out she comes as white as snow; rings on her fingers bells on her toes
Jenny Murray says she'll die if she doesn't get the fella with the roving eye

Let the wind and the rain and the hail blow high and the snow come tumbling from the sky
She's as nice as apple pie and she'll get her own lad by and by
When she gets a lad of her own she won't tell her ma when she goes home
But let them all come as they will; it's Albert Mooney she loves still

(Repeat first verse)

Rosin The Bow

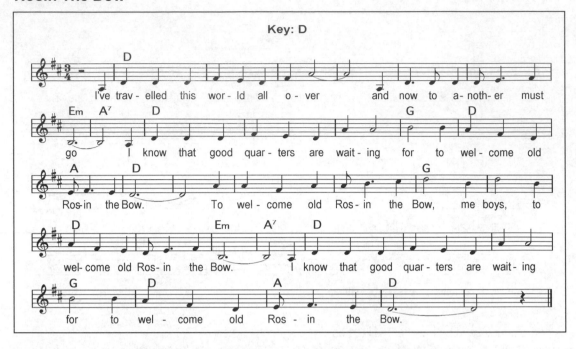

When I'm dead and laid out on the counter; a voice you will hear from below
Saying "Send down a hogshead of whiskey; to drink with old Rosin the Bow"
To drink with old Rosin the Bow, me lads; to drink with old Rosin the Bow
Saying "Send down a hogshead of whiskey; to drink with old Rosin the Bow"

And get a half dozen stout fellows; and stack them all up in a row
Let them drink out of half gallon bottles; to the memory of Rosin the Bow
To the memory of Rosin the Bow, me lads; to the memory of Rosin the Bow
Let them drink out of half gallon bottles; to the memory of Rosin the Bow

Now get this half dozen stout fellows; and let them all stagger and go
And dig a great hole in the meadow; and in it put Rosin the Bow
And in it put Rosin the Bow, me lads; and in it put Rosin the Bow
And dig a great hole in the meadow; and in it put Rosin the Bow

Now get ye a couple of bottles; put one at me head and me toe
With a diamond ring scratch out upon them; the name of old Rosin the Bow
The name of old Rosin the Bow, me lads; the name of old Rosin the Bow
With a diamond ring scratch out upon them; the name of old Rosin the Bow

I feel that old Tyrant approaching; that cruel remorseless old foe
Let me lift up my glass in his honour; take a drink with old Rosin the Bow
Take a drink with old Rosin the Bow, me lads; take a drink with old Rosin the Bow
Let me lift up my glass in his honour; take a drink with old Rosin the Bow

Peggy Gordon

I'm so in love and I can't deny it; my heart is smothered in my breast
It's not for you to let the world know it; a troubled mind sure it knows no rest

I put my head to a glass of brandy; it is my fancy I do declare
For when I'm drinking I'm always thinking; and wishing Peggy Gordon was here

I wish I was in some lonesome valley; where womenkind could not be found
Where little birds sing in the branches; and every moment a different sound

(Repeat the first verse)
(Note that four of the 'C' chords should by played slightly before the relevant note – as per the score)

The Wild Colonial Boy

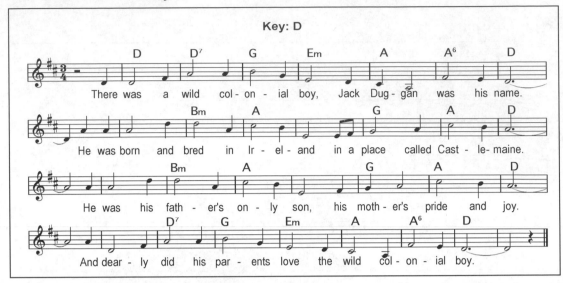

Key: D

There was a wild col-on-ial boy, Jack Dug-gan was his name.

He was born and bred in Ir-el-and in a place called Cast-le-maine.

He was his fath-er's on-ly son, his moth-er's pride and joy.

And dear-ly did his par-ents love the wild col-on-ial boy.

At the early age of sixteen years he left his native home
And to Australia's sunny shores he was inclined to roam
He helped the poor he robbed the rich, their crops he would destroy
A terror to Australia was the Wild Colonial Boy

For two long years this daring youth ran on his wild career
With a heart that knew no danger and a soul that felt no fear
He held the Beechwood Coach up and he robbed Judge McEvoy
Who, trembling, gave his gold up to the Wild Colonial Boy

He bade the Judge "Good Morning" and he told him to beware
For he never robbed an honest judge who acted 'on the square'
"Yet you would rob a mother of her only pride and joy
And breed a race of outlaws like the Wild Colonial Boy"

One morning on the prairie while Jack Duggan rode along
While listening to the mocking bird a-singing out his song
Out jumped three troopers fierce and grim, Kelly, Davis and Fitzroy
Were detailed for to capture him, the Wild Colonial Boy

"Surrender now Jack Duggan, you can see we're three to one
Surrender in our Queen's name for you are a plund'ring son"
Jack drew two pistols from his belt and glared upon Fitzroy
"I'll fight but not surrender!" cried the Wild Colonial Boy

He fired a shot at Kelly and he brought him to the ground
He fired a shot at Davis too, who fell dead at the sound
But a bullet pierced his brave young heart from the pistol of Fitzroy
And that was how they captured him, the Wild Colonial Boy

~~~~~~~~~~~~~~~

Love Is Teasing

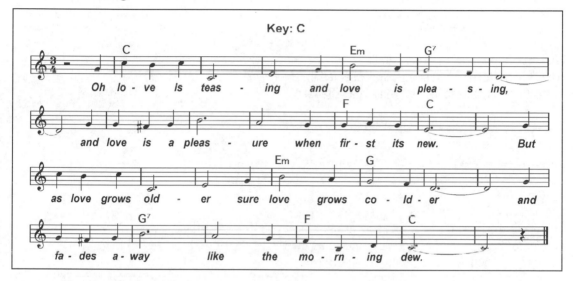

I left my father, I left my mother; I left all my sisters and brothers too
I left all my friends and my own relations; I left them all for to follow you. *Chorus*

And love and porter make a young man older; and love and whiskey make an old man grey
What cannot be cured, love, must be endured, love; and now I am bound for Americay. *Chorus*

The sweetest apple is soonest rotten; the hottest love is the soonest cold
What cannot be cured, love, must be endured, love; and now I am bound for Americay. *Chorus*

I wish, I wish, I wish in vain; I wish that I was a maid again
But a maid again I can never be; till apples grow on an ivy tree. *Chorus*

The Enniskillen Dragoon

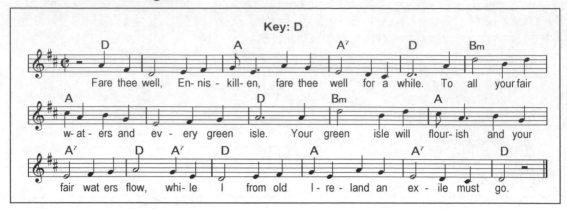

Fare thee well, En-nis-kill-en, fare thee well for a while. To all your fair w-at-ers and ev-ery green isle. Your green isle will flour-ish and your fair wat-ers flow, whi-le I from old I-re-land an ex-ile must go.

Oh they were all dressed out just like gentlemen's' sons
With their bright shining swords and new carbine guns
With their silver mounted pistols she observed them full soon
All because that she loved her Enniskillen Dragoon

The bright sons of Mars as they stood to the right
Their armour did shine like the bright stars at night
She says "Lovely Willie, you've enlisted too soon
To serve as a Royal Enniskillen Dragoon"

"Oh beautiful Flora your pardon I crave
From now and forever I will act as your slave
Your parents insult you both morning and noon
For fear you should wed your Enniskillen Dragoon"

"Oh now, dearest Willie you should mind what you say
Until I am of age my parents I must obey
But when you're leaving Ireland they will surely change their tune
Saying 'The Lord be he with you Enniskillen Dragoon' "

Farewell Enniskillen fare thee well for a while
And all around the borders of Erin's green isle
And when the wars are over I'll return in full bloom
And they'll all welcome home their Enniskillen Dragoon

Now the war is over they've returned home at last
The regiment's in Dublin and Willie got a pass
Last Sunday they were married and bold Willie was the groom
And now she enjoys her Enniskillen Dragoon

The Banks Of The Roses

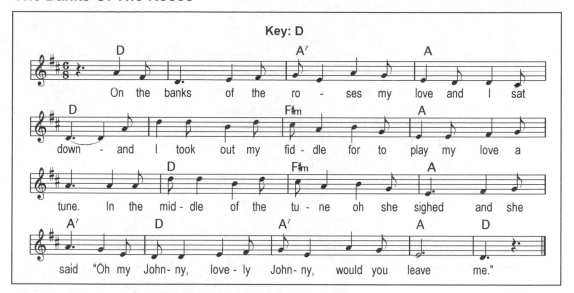

"When I was just a young girl I heard my father say
'I'd sooner see you dead, my girl, and buried in the clay
Rather than be married to a roving runaway
On the lovely sweet banks of the roses' "

Oh well now I am a runaway and sure I'll let you know
That I can take a bottle and drink with anyone
If her father doesn't like me he can keep his daughter home
Then young Johnny will go roving with another

If I ever get wedded 'twill be in the month of May
When the leaves they are green and the meadows they are gay
And me and my true love will sit and sport and play
By the lovely sweet banks of the roses

Arthur McBride

He said "My young fellows if you will enlist; a guinea you quickly will have in your fist
And besides a whole crown for to kick up the dust; and drink the King's health till the morning"
Had we been such fools as to take the advance; with the wee bit of money we'd have to run chance
"For you'd think it no scruples to send us to France; where we would be killed in the morning"

He said "My young fellows if I hear but one word; I instantly now will out with my sword
And into your bodies as strength will afford; so now my gay devils take warning"
But Arthur and I we soon took the odds; and gave them no time for to draw out their blades
Our trusty shillelaghs came over their heads; and paid them right smart in the morning

As for the wee drummer we rifled his pouch; and we made a football of his rowdy-dow-dow
And into the ocean to rock and to roll; and bade him a tedious returning
As for the old rapier that hung by his side; we flung it as far as we could in the tide
"To the devil I pitch you" said Arthur McBride; "to temper your steel in the morning"

The Leaving Of Liverpool

I am sailing upon a Yankee sailing ship; Davy Crockett is her name
And her captain's name is Burgess; and they say she is a floating shame. *Chorus*

Oh the sun is on the harbour love; and I wish I could remain
For I know it will be a long long time; e'er I see you once again. *Chorus*

Follow Me Up To Carlow

Key: D

Lift Mac Cahir Og your face. Brooding o'er the old disgrace that
Black Fitz-will-iam stormed your place and drove you to the
fern. Gray said vic-tor-y was sure, soon the fire-brand he'd sec-ure un-
til he met at Glen-mal-ure with Fiach Mac Hugh O'
Byrne. *Curse and swear Lord Kil-dare, Fiach will do what Fiach will dare.*
Now Fitz-will-iam have a care, fall-en is your star low.
Up with hal-bert out with sword, on we'll go for, by the Lord,
Fiach Mac Hugh has giv-en the word: "Foll-ow me up to Car-low!"

See the swords at Glen Imaal, a-flashing o'er the English Pale
See all the children of the Gael beneath O'Byrne's banners
Rooster of a fighting stock, would you let a Saxon cock
Crow out upon an Irish rock; rise up and teach him manners. ***Chorus***

From Tassagart to Clonmore there flows a stream of Saxon gore
And great is Rory Og O'More at sending the loons to Hades
White is sick, Grey has fled; now for Black Fitzwilliam's head
We'll send it over, dripping red to Queen Liza and her ladies. ***Chorus***

Believe Me, If All Those Endearing Young Charms

It is not while beauty and truth are thine own; and thy cheeks unprofaned by a tear
That the fervour and faith of a soul can be known; to which time will but make thee more dear
No, the heart that has truly loved never forgets; but as truly loves on to the close
As the sun-flower turns on her God when he sets; the same look which she turned when he rose

Easy And Slow

All along Thomas Street, down to the Liffey; the sunshine was gone and the evening grew dark
Along by Kingsbridge and begod in a jiffy; me arms were around her beyond in the Park
Chorus

From city or county the girl she's a jewel; and well made for gripping the most of them are
But any young man he is really a fool; if he tries at the first time to go a bit far
Chorus

Now if you should go to the town of Dungannon; you can search till your eyes they are weary or blind
Be you lying or walking or sitting or running; a lassie like Annie you never will find
Chorus

The Zoological Gardens

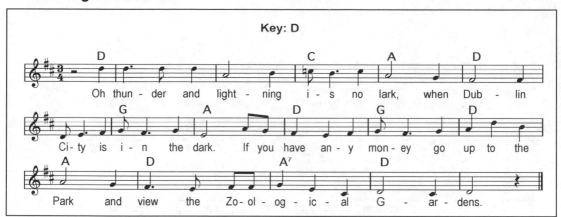

Key: D

Oh thun - der and light - ning i - s no lark, when Dub - lin
Ci- ty is i - n the dark. If you have an - y mon - ey go up to the
Park and view the Zo- ol- og - ic - al G - ar - dens.

Last Sunday night we had no dough; so I took the mot up to see the Zoo
We saw the lions and kangaroos; inside the Zoological Gardens

We went up there by Castleknock; said the mot to me "Sure we'll court by the lough"
And I knew she was one of the rare auld stock; inside the Zoological Gardens

Said the mot to me "My dear friend Jack; would you like a ride on the elephant's back?
If you don't get outta that I'll give you such a crack; inside the Zoological Gardens"

We went up there on our honeymoon; says she to me "If you don't come soon
Sure I'll have to jump in with the hairy baboon; inside the Zoological Gardens"

(Repeat first verse)

Town Of Ballybay

She had a wooden leg that was hollow down the middle
She used to tie a string on it and play it like a fiddle
She fiddled in the hall and she fiddled in the alleyway
She didn't give a damn she had to fiddle anyway. *Chorus*

She said she couldn't dance unless she had her wellie on
But when she had it on she could dance as well as anyone
She wouldn't go to bed unless she had her shimmy on
But when she had it on she would go as quick as anyone. *Chorus*

She had lovers by the score, every Tom and Dick and Harry
She was courting night and day but still she wouldn't marry
And then she fell in love with a fella with a stammer
When he tried to run away, she hit him with a hammer. *Chorus*

She had childer up the stairs, she had childer in the brier
Another ten or twelve sitting roaring by the fire
She fed them on potatoes and on soup she made with nettles
And on lumps of hairy bacon that she boiled up in a kettle. *Chorus*

She led a sheltered life, eating porridge and black puddin'
And she terrorised her man till he up'd and died right sudden
And when the husband died she was feeling very sorry
So she rolled him in a bag and she threw him in a quarry. *Chorus*

The Sally Gardens

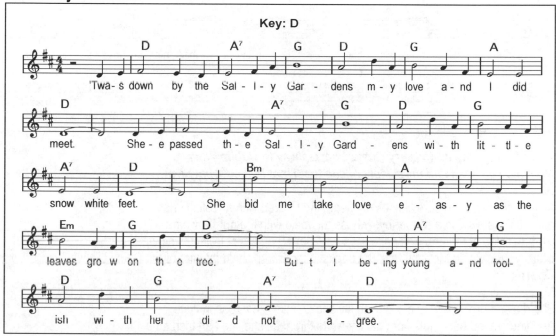

In a field down by the river my love and I did stand
And on my leaning shoulder she laid her snow-white hand
She bid me take life easy as the grass grows on the weirs
But I was young and foolish and now am full of tears

(Repeat first verse)

Star Of The County Down

(The chorus melody is the same as the last two lines of the verse)

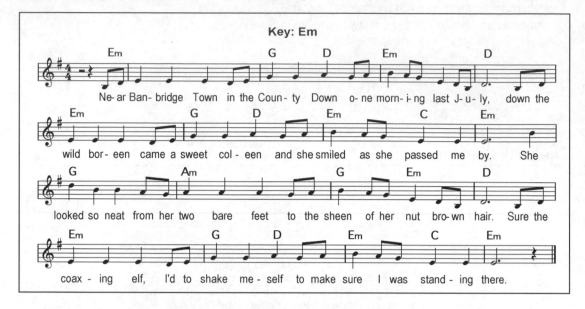

Key: Em

Ne- ar Ban- bridge Town in the Coun- ty Down o- ne morn- i- ng last J- u- ly, down the

wild bor- een came a sweet col- een and she smiled as she passed me by. She

looked so neat from her two bare feet to the sheen of her nut bro- wn hair. Sure the

coax - ing elf, I'd to shake me - self to make sure I was stand - ing there.

From Bantry Bay up to Derry Quay; from Galway to Dublin Town
No maid I've seen like the sweet colleen that I met in the County Down

As she onward sped sure I shook my head and I gazed with a feeling quare
And I said, says I, to a passer-by; "whose the maid with the nut-brown hair?"
Oh he smiled at me and with pride says he; "that's the gem of Ireland's crown
She's young Rosie McCann from the banks of the Bann; she's the star of the County Down"
Chorus

She'd a soft brown eye and a look so sly and a smile like a rose in June
And you craved each note from her lily-white throat as she lilted an Irish tune
At the pattern dance you'd be held in trance as she tripped through a jig or a reel
When her eyes she'd roll she would lift your soul and your heart she would quickly steal
Chorus

Now I've roamed a bit but was never hit since my travelling days began
But fair and square I surrendered there to the charms of young Rosie McCann
With my heart to let sure no tenant yet did I meet with a shawl or a gown
But in she went and I asked no rent from the Star of the County Down
Chorus

At the cross-roads fair I'll be surely there and I'll dress in my Sunday clothes
With me shoes all bright and me hat cocked right for a smile from the nut-brown rose
No pipe I'll smoke and no horse I'll yoke let my plough with the rust turn brown
Till a smiling bride by my own fireside be the star of the County Down
Chorus

~~~~~~~~~~~~~~

I Never Will Marry

(Verses and chorus have the same melody)

One day as I rambled down by the seashore
The wind it did whistle and the waters did roar
I heard a young maiden make a pitiful cry
She sounded so lonesome at the waters nearby. *Chorus*

"The shells in the ocean will be my death bed
May the fish in the waters swim over my head
My love's gone and left me; he's the one I adore
I never will see him, no never, no more". *Chorus*

She plunged her fair body in the water so deep
She closed her pretty blue eyes in the waters to sleep
And that lonesome maiden and her pitiful cries
Can be heard from the ocean to the heavenly skies. *Chorus*

The Wearing Of The Green

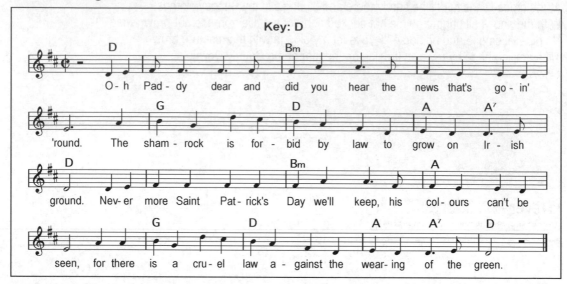

Key: D

O-h Pad-dy dear and did you hear the news that's go-in' 'round. The sham-rock is for-bid by law to grow on Ir-ish ground. Nev-er more Saint Pat-rick's Day we'll keep, his col-ours can't be seen, for there is a cru-el law a-gainst the wear-ing of the green.

I met with Napper Tandy and he took me by the hand
He said "How's poor old Ireland; please tell how does she stand"
"She is the most distressful land that ever yet was seen
For they're hanging men and women for the wearing of the Green"

And if the colour we must wear is England's cruel red
Let it remind us of the blood that Ireland's sons have shed
Then take the shamrock from your hat and cast it on the sod
And never fear, 'twill take root there though under foot 'tis trod

When laws can stop the blades of grass from growing where they grow
And when the leaves in summertime their colours dare not show
Then I will change the colour that I wear in my cáibin*
But 'til that day please God I stay a-wearing of the Green

But if sometime the colour should be torn from Ireland's heart
Her sons with shame and sorrow from our shores will surely part
I've heard a whisper of a land that lies beyond the sea
Where rich and poor stand equal in the light of liberty

So Erin we must leave you now; cast out by tyrant's hand
We'll treasure mother's blessing from a strange and distant land
Where England's cruel and viscous hand is never to be seen
And where, please God, we'll plough the sod, a-wearing of the Green

*Pronounced "cawbeen" (cloth cap)

I Know My Love

Key: D

I know my love by his way of wa-lk-ing I know my love by his way of ta-lk-ing I know my love dressed in his jer-sey blue, and if my love leaves me what will I do-o-o *and still she cried* "I love him the best and a troub-led mind sure it knows no re-e-est" *and still she cried* "Bon-ny boys are few, and if my love leaves me what will I do".

There is a dance house down in Mardyke; 'tis there my true love goes every night
He takes a strange girl upon his knee; and don't you think now that vexes me? *Chorus*

If my love knew I could wash and wring; if my love knew I could weave and spin
I'd make a suit of the finest kind; but the want of money leaves me behind. *Chorus*

I know my love is an arrant rover; I know my love roams the wide world over
In some foreign town he may chance to tarry; and some foreign maid he will surely marry. *Chorus*

The Galway Shawl

(Verses and chorus have the same melody)

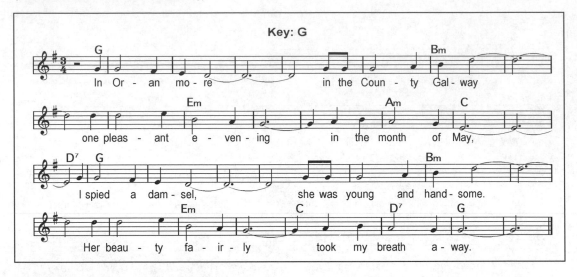

She wore no jewels, no costly diamonds
No paint or powder, no none at all
She wore a bonnet with a ribbon on it
And around her shoulders was a Galway shawl

As we kept on walking she kept on talking
Till her father's cottage came into view
She said "Come in sir, and meet my father
And for to please him play the Foggy Dew". ***Chorus***

I played 'The Blackbird' and 'The Stack of Barley'
'Rodney's Glory' and 'The Foggy Dew'
She sang each note like an Irish linnet
And the tears they flowed in her eyes of blue. ***Chorus***

'Twas early, early, all in the morning
I hit the road for old Donegal
She said "Goodbye sir" and her eyes seemed brighter
And my heart remained with the Galway shawl. ***Chorus***

The Banks Of Claudy

Key: G

'Twas on a pleas - ant mo - rn - ing all i - n the month of May.

Down by the Banks of Cl - au - dy I care - less - ly wound my way.

I o - ver - heard a maid - en and she tear - ful - ly did com - plain,

"It's on the Banks of Clau - dy where my da - rl - ing do re - main".

I boldly stepped up to her, I took her by surprise
I own she did not know me, I being dressed in disguise
"Where are you going my fair one, my joy and heart's delight
Where are you going to wander this cold and windy night?"

"It's on the way to Claudy's banks, if you will please to show
Take pity on a stranger, for there I want to go
It's seven long years or better since Johnny has left this shore
He's crossing the wide ocean, where the foaming billows roar"

"He's crossing the wide ocean for honour and for fame
His ship's been wrecked so I've been told down on the Spanish Main"
"It's on the Banks of Claudy fair maiden whereon you stand
Now don't you believe young Johnny, for he's a false young man"

Now when she heard this dreadful news she fell into despair
For the wringing of her tender hands and the tearing of her hair
"If Johnny he be drowned no man alive I'll take
Through lonesome glens and valleys I'll wander for his sake"

Now when he saw her loyalty no longer could he stand
He fell into her arms saying "Betsy I'm the man".
Saying "Betsy I'm the young man who caused you all the pain,
And since we've met on Claudy's banks we'll never part again"

Quare Bungle Rye

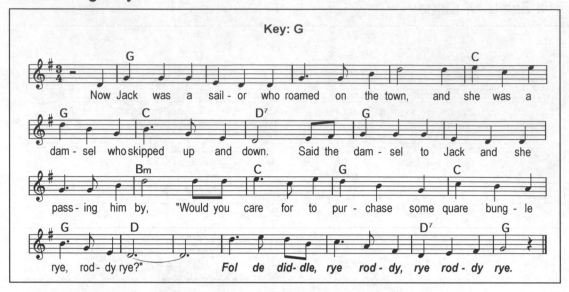

Key: G

Now Jack was a sail-or who roamed on the town, and she was a
dam-sel who skipped up and down. Said the dam-sel to Jack and she
pass-ing him by, "Would you care for to pur-chase some quare bung-le
rye, rod-dy rye?" *Fol de did-dle, rye rod-dy, rye rod-dy rye.*

Thought Jack to himself now what can this be
But the finest of whiskey from old Germany
Smuggled up in a basket and sold on the sly
And the name that it goes by is quare bungle rye roddy rye. *Chorus*

Jack gave her a pound and he thought nothing strange
She said "hold the basket till I run for your change"
Jack looked in the basket and a baby did spy
"Begorra" says he "This is quare bungle rye roddy rye!". *Chorus*

Now to get the child christened was Jack's first intent
And to get the child christened to the parson he went
Said the parson to Jack, "What will he go by?"
"Bedad now", says Jack, "call him quare bungle rye roddy rye". *Chorus*

Now all you bold sailors who roam on the town
Beware of the damsels who skip up and down
Take a look in their baskets as they pass you by
Or else they may sell you some quare bungle rye roddy rye. *Chorus*

Twenty-One Years

Key: C

The judge said "Stand up boy and dry up your tears. You're sen- tenced to Dart- moor for twen- ty one years". So dry up your tears girl and kiss me good- bye. The best friends must part, so must you and must I.

I hear the train coming, 'twill be here at nine
To take me to Dartmoor to serve out my time
I look down the railway and plainly I see
You standing there waiving your goodbyes to me

Six months have gone by, love, I wish I were dead
This cold dreary jail and a stone for my head
It's raining, it's hailing, the moon shows no light
Why won't you tell me, love, why you never write?

I've counted the days, love, I've counted the nights
I've counted the footsteps, I've counted the lights
I've counted the raindrops, I've counted the stars
I've counted a million of these prison bars

I've waited, I've trusted, I've longed for the day
A lifetime so lonely; my hair's turning grey
My thoughts are for you, love, till I'm out of my mind
For twenty-one years is a mighty long time

The Mermaid

Then up spoke the captain of our gallant ship and a fine old man was he
"This fishy mermaid has warned me of our doom. We will sink to the bottom of the sea". *Chorus*

Then up spoke the mate of our gallant ship and a fine spoken man was he
Saying "I have a wife in Brooklyn by the sea and tonight a widow she will be". *Chorus*

Then up spoke the cabin-boy of our gallant ship and a brave young lad was he
"I have a sweetheart in Salem by the sea and tonight she'll be weeping for me". *Chorus*

Then up spoke the cook of our gallant ship and a crazy old butcher was he
"I care so much more for my skillets and my pans than I do for the bottom of the sea". *Chorus*

Then three times around spun our gallant ship and three times around spun she
Three times around spun our gallant ship and she sank to the bottom of the sea. *Chorus*

Sean South From Garryowen

And as they moved along the street up to the barracks door
They scorned the dangers they would meet; the fate that lay in store
They were fighting for old Ireland's cause to claim their very own
And their leader was a Limerick man, Sean South from Garryowen

But the sergeant spied their daring plan, he spied them through the door
With their sten guns and their rifle shots a hail of death did roar
And when that awful night had passed two men lay cold as stone
And one was from a border town and one from Garryowen

No more he'll hear the seagulls cry o'er the murmuring Shannon tide
For he fell beneath a northern sky, brave Hanlon by his side
He has gone to join that gallant band of Plunkett, Pearce and Tone
Another martyr for old Ireland, Sean South from Garryowen

The Black Velvet Band

(Verses and chorus have the same melody)

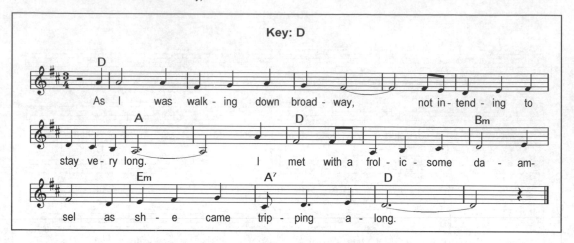

A gold watch she took out of her pocket and placed it right into my hand
On the very first time that I saw her; bad luck to the black velvet band

Her eyes they shone like diamonds; you'd think she was queen of the land
With her hair thrown over her shoulder; tied up with a black velvet band

'Twas in the town of Kilkenny; an apprentice to trade I was bound
With gaiety and bright amusement to see all the days go around
Till misfortune and trouble came over me which forced me to stray from the land
Far away from my friends and relations; betrayed by the black velvet band. *Chorus*

Before judge and jury next morning the both of us did appear
A gentleman swore to his jewellery and the case against us was clear
Seven long years' transportation away down to Van Diemen's Land
Far away from my friends and relations to follow the black velvet band. *Chorus*

Now all you brave young Irish lads a warning please gather from me
Beware of the pretty young damsels you meet all around Kilkenny
They'll treat you with whiskey and porter until you're unable to stand
And before you have time for to leave them you'll be sent down to Van Diemen's Land. *Chorus*

Look At The Coffin

Look at the flowers, all bloody withered; isn't it grand boys to be bloody-well dead
Chorus

Look at the mourners, bloody great hypocrites; isn't it grand boys to be bloody-well dead
Chorus

Look at the preacher, bloody sanctimonious; isn't it grand boys to be bloody-well dead
Chorus

Let Him Go, Let Him Tarry

(Verses and chorus have the same melody)

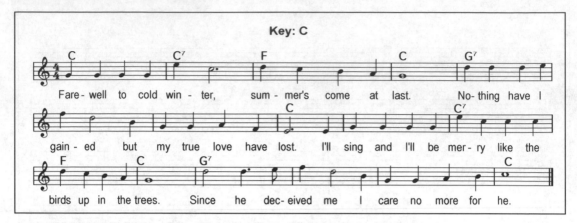

Let him go, let him tarry, let him sink or let him swim
He doesn't care for me nor I don't care for him
He can go and get another that I hope he will enjoy
For I'm going to marry a far nicer boy

He wrote me a letter saying he was very bad
I sent him back an answer saying I was awful glad
He wrote me another saying he was well and strong
But I care no more for him than the ground he walks upon. *Chorus*

Some of his friends they have a good kind wish for me
Others of his friends sure they could hang me on a tree
But soon I'll let them see my love and soon I'll let them know
That I can get a new sweetheart at any place I go. *Chorus*

He can go to his old mother now and set her mind at ease
I hear she's an old woman and very hard to please
It's slighting me and talking ill is what she's always done
Because I was courting her great big ugly son. *Chorus*

The Golden Jubilee
(Verses and chorus have the same melody)

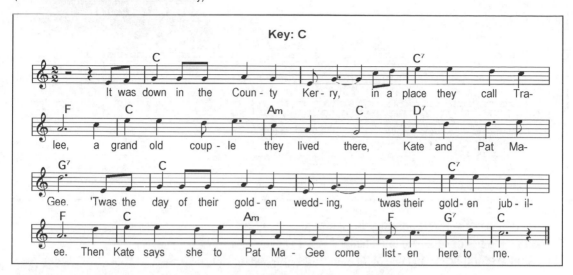

Put on your old knee britches and your coat of emerald green
Take off that hat me darling Pat, put on your old cáibín*
For today's our Golden Wedding and I'll have you all to know
Just how we looked when we were wed fifty years ago

Oh well do I remember how we danced on the village green
You held me in your arms dear Pat and called me your colleen
Your hair was like a raven's wing but now it's turning grey
Come over here my sweetheart dear and hear what I've to say. *Chorus*

Oh well do I remember when first I was your bride
In the little chapel on the hill where we stood side by side
Of good friends we've had plenty, of troubles we've had few
Come over here my sweetheart dear and here's what you must do. *Chorus*

*Pronounced "cawbeen" (cloth cap)

Three Lovely Lassies From Kimmage

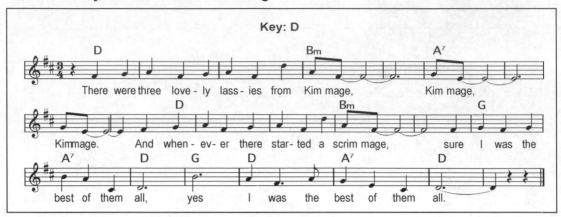

Key: D

There were three love-ly lass-ies from Kimmage, Kimmage,
Kimmage. And when-ev-er there star-ted a scrim-mage, sure I was the
best of them all, yes I was the best of them all.

Well the cause of the row is Joe Cashin, Joe Cashin, Joe Cashin
For he told me he thought I looked smashin'
At the dance at the Adelaide Hall; at the dance at the Adelaide Hall

He told me he thought we should marry, should marry, should marry
For he said it was foolish to tarry
So he lent me the price of the ring; so he lent me the price of the ring

When he has a few jars he goes frantic, goes frantic, goes frantic
But he's tall and he's dark and romantic
And I love him in spite of it all; and I love him in spite of it all

Well me dad said he'd give us a present, a present, a present
A picture of a lovely pheasant
The picture will hang on the wall; yes the picture will hang on the wall

I went to the Tenancy Section, the Section, the Section
The T.D.* before the election
Said he'd get me a house near me ma; said he's get me a house near me ma

Well I'll get a house the man said it, said it, said it
When I've five or six kids to me credit
In the meantime we'll live with me ma; in the meantime we'll live with me ma

*Irish member of Parliament

Maids When You're Young

(Verses and chorus have the same melody)

For he's got no folurum fol diddle-i-urum da
He's got no folurum fol diddle-i-aye
He's got no flurum, he's lost his ding-durum da
Maids when you're young never wed an auld man

When we went to church, hey ding-durum da
When we went to church me being young
When we went to church he left me in the lurch
Maids when you're young never wed an auld man. *Chorus*

When we went to bed, hey ding-durum da
When we went to bed me being young
When we went to bed he lay like he was dead
Maids when you're young never wed an auld man. *Chorus*

I threw my leg over him hey ding-durum da
I threw my leg over him me being young
I threw my leg over him, damn nearly smothered him
Maids when you're young never wed an auld man. *Chorus*

When he went to sleep, hey ding-durum da
When he went to sleep me being young
When he went to sleep out of bed I did creep
Into the arms of a willing young man
Chorus change:- "And I found his falurum, fol diddle-i-urum da", etc.

The Boys Of Fairhill

Key: D

| D | Bm | A | A⁷ |

Come and have a hol - i - day with our hurl - ing club so gay. Your

souls we will charm and your hearts we will thrill. The

girls sure they will cha - rm you. The boys sure they won't ha - rm you.

"Here's up them all!", says the Boys of Fair - hill.

We'll go down by Sunday's Well, what might happen, who can tell
Heads, they might roll or some blood it might spill
We'll come back by Blackpool way when we've overcome the fray
"Here's up them all!" says the Boys of Fairhill

Jimmy Barry hooks the ball, we'll hook Jimmy, ball and all
"Here's up them all!" says the Boys of Fairhill
The Rockies thought they were the stars till they met the Saint Finbarr's
"Here's up them all!" says the Boys of Fairhill

Kathy Barry sells crubeens, fairly bursting at the seams
Sure for to cure and more sure for to kill
The stench on Patrick's Bridge is wicked, how does Father Matthew stick it
"Here's up them all!" says the Boys of Fairhill

The Waxie's Dargle

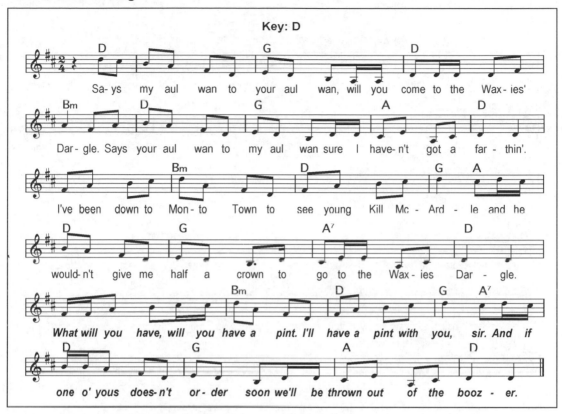

Key: D

Says my oul' one to your oul' one "Will ye come to the Galway Races?"
Says your oul' one to my oul' one "With the price of me oul' lad's braces
I went down to Capel Street to the Jewman moneylender
But they wouldn't give me a couple of bob for me oul' lad's new suspenders". *Chorus*

Says my oul' one to your oul' one "We have no beef or mutton"
But if we go down to Monto town we might get a drink for nothin'
Here's a piece of advice for you which I got from an oul' fishmonger
When food is scarce and you see the hearse you'll know you died of hunger". *Chorus*

The Snowy-Breasted Pearl

Oh thou blooming milk-white dove to whom I have aimed my love
Do not ever thus reprove my constancy
Now there are maidens would be mine with a wealth in land and kine
If my heart would but incline to turn from thee
But a kiss with welcome bland and a touch of thy fair hand
Are all that I demand, would'st thou not spurn
For if thou be not mine dear girl
Oh, thou snowy-breasted pearl
May I never from the fair with life return

Slievenamon

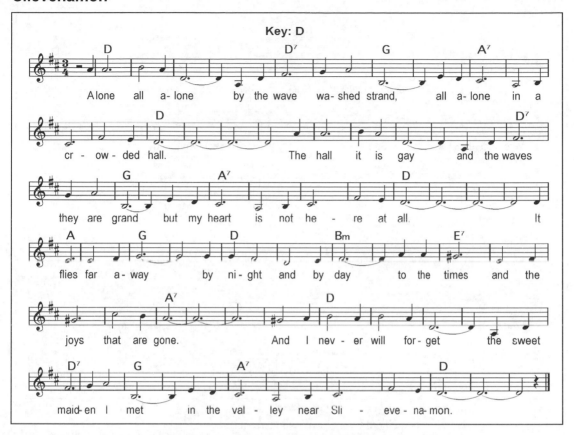

'Twas not the grace of her queenly air; nor her cheek of the rose's glow
Nor her soft dark eyes or her flowing hair; nor was it her lily-white brow
'Twas the soul of truth and of melting youth and a smile like the summer's dawn
That stole my heart away on that soft summer day in the Valley near Slievenamon

In the Festival Hall by the wave-washed shore, there my restless spirit cries
"My love, oh my love, shall I ne'er see you more and my land will you never uprise?"
By night and by day, I ever ever pray while so lonely my life flows on
But to see our flag unrolled and my true-love to enfold in the Valley near Slievenamon

The Spanish Lady

Key: G

As I rode down through Dub-lin c-i-ty at the hour of twelve at night,

who should I see but a Span-ish l-a-dy wash-ing her feet by can-dle - light.

First she washed them then she dried them o-ver a fire of am-ber coal. In

all my life I ne'er did see a - a maid so sweet a - bout the soul.

Whack fol the toor-a - loor-a la-ad-ie whack fol the toor - a - loor-a lay.

Whack fol the toor-a - loor-a la-ad-ie whack fol the toor - a - loor-a lay.

As I came back through Dublin city at the hour of half past eight
Who should I spy but the Spanish Lady brushing her hair in the broad daylight
First she tossed it then she brushed it; on her lap was a silver comb
In all my life I ne'er did see a maid so fair since I did roam. *Chorus*

As I went back through Dublin city as the sun began to set
Who should I spy but the Spanish Lady catching a moth in a golden net
When she saw me then she fled me, lifting her petticoat over her knee
In all my life I ne'er did see a maid so shy as the Spanish Lady. *Chorus*

I wandered north and I wandered south through Stoneybatter and Patrick's Close
Up and around by the Gloucester Diamond and back by Napper Tandy's house
Old age has laid her hand upon me, cold as a fire of ashy coals
In all my life I ne'er did see a maid so sweet as the Spanish Lady. *Chorus*

Highland Paddy

And in the morning we rose early, just before the break of dawn
Blackbirds singing in the bushes, greetings to a smiling morn
Gather 'round me men of Ireland, all ye Fenians gather round
Hand to hand with sword and musket, spill the blood upon this holy ground. *Chorus*

There is a glen beside the river, just outside Kilkenny town
There we met this noble captain, men lay dying upon the ground
There is a grave down by the river, a mile outside Kilkenny town
There we laid our noble Captain, birds were silent when this Fenian died. *Chorus*

For all my life I will remember, I'll remember night and day
That once I rode into Kilkenny and I heard the noble Captain say. *Chorus*

Paddy's Green Shamrock Shore

Key: C

Oh fa - re thee well sweet I - re - la - n - d my o - wn dear na - tive home. It brea - ks my heart, t - o se - e friends part for it's then that the tear- drops will fall. I'm o - n my way to A - m - er - ic - ay will I e'er see my home land once more. For n - ow I leave my o - wn true lo - ve on Pad - dy's green sham - rock shore.

Our ship she lies at anchor now; she's standing by the quay
May fortune bright shine down each night as we sail all across the sea
Many ships have been lost, many lives it has cost on the journey that lies before
With a tear in my eye I'm bidding goodbye to Paddy's green shamrock shore

From Londonderry we did set sail; it being the fourth of May
On a sturdy ship to cover the trip across to Americay
Fresh water then did we take in; one hundred barrels or more
For fear we'd be short before reaching port far from the shamrock shore

Two of our anchors we did weigh before we left the quay
All down the river we were towed till we came to the open sea
We saw that night the grandest sight we ever saw before
The sun going down 'tween sea and sky far from Paddy's green shamrock shore

Early next morn, sea-sick and forlorn, not one of us was free
And I myself was confined to bed with no one to pity me
No father or mother or sister or brother to raise my head when sore
That made me think of the family I left back on Paddy's green shamrock shore

So fare thee well my own true love I think of you night and day
A place in my mind you surely will find although I'm so far away
Though I am alone and away from my home I'll think of the good time before
Until the day I can make my way back to Paddy's green shamrock shore

Cockles And Mussels

(also known as "Molly Malone")

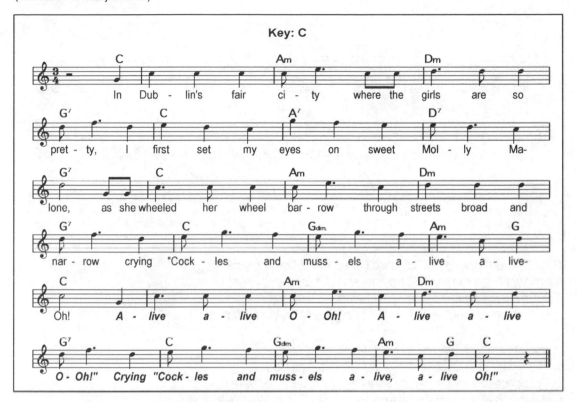

She was a fishmonger and sure 'twas no wonder
For so was her father and mother before
And they both wheeled their barrows through streets broad and narrow
Crying "Cockles and mussels, alive, alive-oh!" *Chorus*

She died of a fever and no one could save her
And that was the end of sweet Molly Malone
Now her ghost wheels her barrow through streets broad and narrow
Crying "Cockles and mussels, alive, alive-oh!" *Chorus*

Muirsheen Durkin

(Verses and chorus have the same melody)

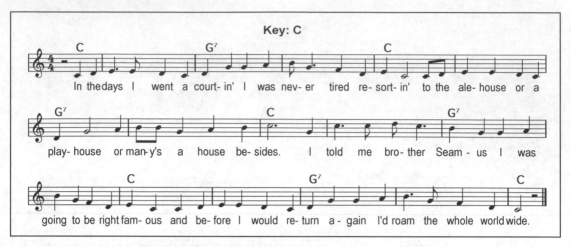

Key: C

In the days I went a court-in' I was nev-er tired re-sort-in' to the ale-house or a play-house or man-y's a house be-sides. I told me bro-ther Seam-us I was going to be right fam-ous and be-fore I would re-turn a-gain I'd roam the whole world wide.

Goodbye Muirsheen Durkin, sure I'm sick and tired of workin'
No more I'll dig the praties, no longer I'll be fooled
For sure's me name is Carney I'll be off to Californee
And instead of digging praties I'll be digging lumps of gold

I've courted girls in Blarney, in Kanturk and in Killarney
In Passage and in Queenstown; that is the Cobh of Cork
But goodbye to all this pleasure sure I'm off to seek me leisure
And the next time you will hear from me is a letter from New York. *Chorus*

So goodbye all ye boys at home I'm sailing far across the foam
I'm going to make me fortune in far Americay
There's gold and money plenty for the poor and for the gentry
And when I do return again I never more will stray. *Chorus*

Kelly From Killane

Key: C

"What's the news, what's the news, O my bold Shel-ma-lier, with your long barr-elled gu-n of the sea? Say what wind from the sun blows his mess-en-ger here with a hymn of the da-wn for the free?" "Good-ly news, good-ly news do I bring, youth of Forth! Good-ly news shall you hear, Bar-gy man! For the boys march at morn from the South to the North, led by Kel-ly, the bo-y from Kil-lane".

"Tell me who is that giant with the gold curling hair; he who rides at the head of your band
Seven feet is his height with some inches to spare; and he looks like a king in command"
"Ah my lads, that's the pride of the bold Shelmaliers; 'mongst our greatest of heroes, a man
Fling your beavers aloft and give three ringing cheers; for John Kolly, the boy from Killane"

Enniscorthy's in flames and old Wexford is won; and the Barrow, tomorrow, we will cross
On a hill o'er the town we have planted a gun; that will batter the gateway of Ross
All the Forth men and Bargy men march o'er the heath; with brave Harvey to lead on the van
But the foremost of all in that grim gap of death; will be Kelly, the boy from Killane

But the gold sun of freedom grew darkened at Ross; and it set by the Slaney's red waves
And poor Wexford, stripped naked, hung high on a cross; and her heart pierced by traitors and slaves
Glory O! Glory O! To her brave sons who died; for the cause of long downtrodden man
Glory O! To Mount Leinster's own darling and pride; dauntless Kelly, the boy from Killane

Roddy McCorley

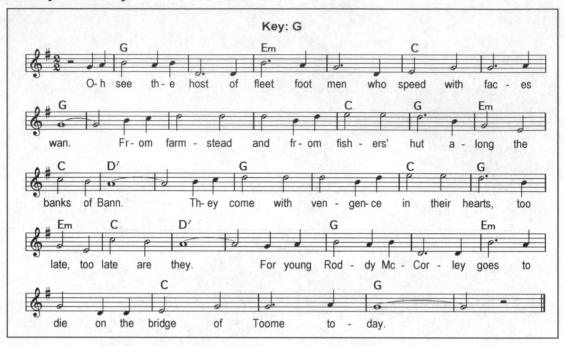

When he last stepped up that street, his shining pike in hand
Behind him marched in grim array a stalwart earnest band
For Antrim town, for Antrim town he led them to the fray
And young Roddy McCorley goes to die on the bridge of Toome today

Up the narrow streets he boldly steps, smiling, proud and young
Around the hemp rope on his neck his golden ringlets clung
There was never a tear in his blue eyes, both sad and bright are they
For young Roddy McCorley goes to die on the bridge of Toome today

There was never a one of all our dead more bravely fell in fray
Than he who marches to his fate on the bridge of Toome today
True to the last as we say goodbye he treads the upward way
And young Roddy McCorley goes to die on the bridge of Toome today

A Nation Once Again

When boy-ho-od's fire was in my blood I read of a-n-ci-ent free men. For
Greece a-nd Rome who brave-ly stood three hun-dred me n a-nd three men. And
then I prayed I yet might see our fet-ters rent in twain, a-nd Ire-land long a
prov ince be a na-tion once a-gain. A na-tion once a-gain. A na-tion once a-
gain. And Ire-la-nd long a-a prov-en-ce be, a-a na-tion once a-gain.

And from that time through wildest woe that hope has shone a far light
Nor could love's brightest summer glow, outshine that solemn starlight
It seemed to watch above my head in forum field and fane
Its angel voice sang 'round my head, a nation once again *Chorus*

It whispered too that freedom's ark and service high and holy
Would be profaned by feelings dark and passions vain or lowly
For freedom comes from God's right hand and needs a godly train
And righteous men must make our land a nation once again. *Chorus*

So as I grew from boy to man I bent me to that bidding
My spirit of each selfish plan and cruel passion ridding
For thus I hoped some day to aid; oh can such hope be vain
When my dear country can be made a nation once again. *Chorus*

The Moonshiner

(Verses and chorus have the same melody)

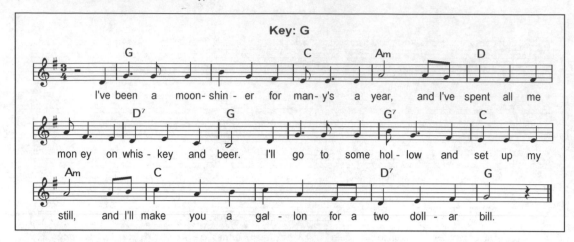

Key: G

I've been a moon-shin-er for man-y's a year, and I've spent all me mon-ey on whis-key and beer. I'll go to some hol-low and set up my still, and I'll make you a gal-lon for a two doll-ar bill.

I'm a rambler, I'm a gambler, I'm a long way from home
And if you don't like me then leave me alone
I'll eat when I'm hungry, I'll drink when I'm dry
And if the moonshine don't kill me I'll live till I die

I'll go to some hollow in this country
Ten gallons of wash and I'll go on a spree
No woman to follow and the world is all mine
I love none so well as I love the moonshine. *Chorus*

Moonshine, dear moonshine, oh how I love thee
You killed my poor father but dare you try me
Bless all the moonshiners and bless the moonshine
Its breath smells as sweet as the dew on the vine. *Chorus*

There's moonshine for Molly and moonshine for May
Moonshine for Tom and he'll sing all the day
Moonshine for me breakfast and moonshine for me tea
Moonshine oh me hearties! It's moonshine for me. *Chorus*

Mush Mush

(Verses and chorus have the same melody)

Singing mush mush mush toor-a-lie-addy; sing mush mush mush toor-a-lie-ay
There was ne'er a gassoon* in the village dared tread on the tail of me coat

'Twas there I learned all of my courting; many lessons I took in the art
Till Cupid the blackguard, in sporting; an arrow drove straight through my heart
Molly Connor she lived right beside me; and tender lines to her I wrote
If you dare say one wrong word against her; I'll tread on the tail of your coat. **Chorus**

But a blackguard called Mickey Moloney; he stole her affections away
He had money and I hadn't any; so I sent him a challenge next day
That evening we met at the woodbine; the Shannon we crossed in a boat
And I leathered him with my shillelagh; for he trod on the tail of my coat. *Chorus*

My fame spread abroad through the nation; and folks came a-flocking to see
And they cried out without hesitation; "You're a fighting man, Billy McGee"
I cleaned out the Finnegan faction; and I licked all the Murphys afloat
If you're in for a row or a ruction just tread on the tail of me coat. *Chorus*

* Young boy

Reilly's Daughter

Key: G

As I was sit-ting by the fire, eat-ing spuds and drink-ing por-ter, sud-den-ly a thought came in-to my mind: I think I'll mar-ry old Reil-ly's daugh-ter! *Gid-dy - i - ay, gid-dy - i - ay, gid-dy-i - ay for the one eyed Reil-ly, gid-dy-i - ay. (Boom Boom Boom). Bang it on your old bass drum!*

For Reilly played on the big bass drum
Reilly had a mind for murder and slaughter
Reilly had one big red glittering eye
And he kept that eye on his lovely daughter. *Chorus*

Her hair was black and her eyes were blue
The Colonel and the Major and the Captain sought her
The Sergeant and the Private and the drummer boy too
But they never had a chance with aul' Reilly's daughter. *Chorus*

I got me a ring and a parson too
I got me a scratch in the married quarter
Settled me down to a peaceful life
As happy as a king with Reilly's daughter. *Chorus*

I hear a sudden footstep on the stair
It's the one-eyed Reilly and he lookin' for slaughter
With two pistols in his hand
Searching for the man who had married his daughter. *Chorus*

I took auld Reilly by the hair
Rammed his head into a bucket of water
Fired his pistols in the air
A damned sight quicker than I married his daughter. *Chorus*

The Gypsy

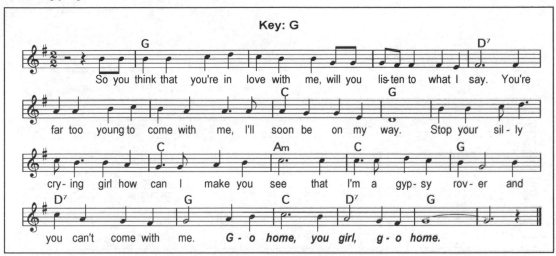

Key: G

So you think that you're in love with me, will you lis-ten to what I say. You're far too young to come with me, I'll soon be on my way. Stop your sil - ly cry - ing girl how can I make you see that I'm a gyp - sy rov - er and you can't come with me. *G - o home, you girl, g - o home.*

You met me at the marketplace when your Ma was not with you
You liked my long brown ringlets and my handkerchief of blue
Although I'm very fond of you and you asked me home to tea
I am a gypsy rover and you can't come with me. *Chorus*

Your brother is a peeler and he would put me in jail
If he knew I was a poacher and I hunt your lord's best game
Your daddy is a gentleman, your mammy's just as grand
But I'm a gypsy rover; I'll not be your husband. *Chorus*

The hour is drawing on my love and your ma's expecting thee
Don't you say you met me here for I'm just a gypsy
Please let go my jacket now; your love will have to wait
For I am twenty-two years old and you are only eight. *Chorus*

The Cliffs Of Doneen

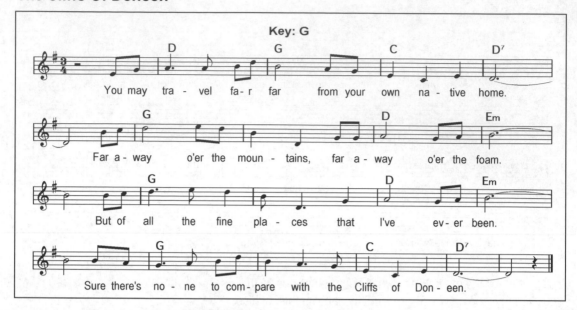

It's a nice place to be on a fine summer's day
Watching all the wild flowers that ne'er do decay
Oh the hares and the pheasants are plain to be seen
Making homes for their young 'round the Cliffs of Doneen

Take a view o'er the mountains, fine sights you'll see there
You'll see the high rocky mountains o'er the west coast of Clare
Oh the towns of Kilkee and Kilrush can be seen
From the high rocky slopes 'round the cliffs of Doneen

Fare thee well to Doneen, fare thee well for a while
And to all the kind people I'm leaving behind
To the streams and the meadows where late I have been
And the high rocky slopes 'round the Cliffs of Doneen

Fare thee well to Doneen, fare thee well for a while
And although we are parted by the raging sea wild
Once again I will wander with my Irish colleen
'Round the high rocky slopes of the Cliffs of Doneen

The Meeting Of The Waters

Key: G

There is not in this wide world a val - ley so sweet, as the vale in whose
bos- om the bright wat - ers meet. Oh the last rays o - f feel - ing and
life must de- part, e'er the bloom of that val - ley shall fade from my
heart. E'er the bloom of that val - ley shall fade from my heart.

Yet it was not that Nature had shed o'er the scene
Her purest of crystal and brightest of green
'Twas not her soft magic of streamlet or hill
Oh no! It was something more exquisite still
Oh no! It was something more exquisite still

'Twas that friends, the belov'd of my bosom were near
Who made every dear scene of enchantment more dear
And who felt how the best charms of Nature improve
When we see them reflected from looks that we love
When we see them reflected from looks that we love

Sweet vale of Avoca how calm could I rest
In thy bosom of shade with the friends I love best
Where the storms that we feel in this cold world should cease
And our hearts like thy waters be mingled in peace
And our hearts like thy waters be mingled in peace

The Jug Of Punch

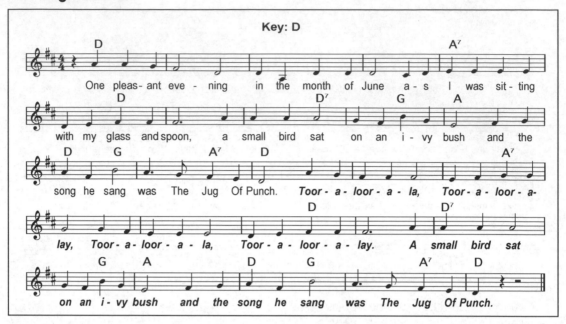

What more diversion can a man desire than to sit him down by a snug coal fire
And upon his knee have a pretty wench and upon his table a jug of punch. *Chorus*

If I was sickly and very bad and was not able for to go or stand
I would not think it at all amiss for to pledge my shoes for a jug of punch. *Chorus*

The doctor fails with all his art to cure an impression on the heart
If life was gone but within an inch, what would bring it back but a jug of punch. *Chorus*

But when I'm dead and within my grave no costly tombstone will I have
They'll dig a grave both wide and deep with a jug of punch at my head and feet. *Chorus*

I'm A Rover

(Verses and chorus have the same melody)

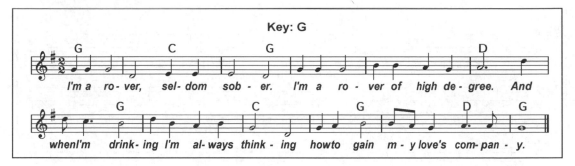

Though the night be dark as dungeon; not a star to be seen above
I will be guided without a stumble into the arms of the one I love

He stepped up to her bedroom window kneeling gently upon a stone
And he tapped at the bedroom window; "Darling dear, do you lie alone?" *Chorus*

"It's only me dear your own true lover; open up please and let me in
For I have travelled a weary journey and I'm near drenched to my skin"

She opened up with the greatest pleasure; unlocked the door and she let him in
They both shook hands and embraced each other; till the morning they lay as one. *Chorus*

The cocks were waking the birds were whistling; the streams they ran free about the brae
"Remember lass I'm a ploughman's laddie and the farmer I must obey"

"Now my love I must go and leave thee and though the hills they are high above
I will climb them with greater pleasure for I've gained your undying love". *Chorus*

The Boys From The County Armagh

Key: G

There's one fair coun-ty in Ire-land with mem-ories so glor-ious and grand. Where nat-ure has lav-ished her beau-ty in the or-chards of Er-in's green land. I love its Cath-ed-er-al ci-ty once foun-ded by Pat-rick so true, and it bears in the heart of its bos-om the ash-es of Bri-an Bo-ru. It's my own Ir-ish home, far a-cross the foam. Al-though I've of-ten left it, in for-eign lands to roam. No mat-ter where I wan-der through cit-ies near or far, sure my heart is at home in old Ire-land, in the coun-ty of Ar-magh.

I've travelled that part of the county, through Newtown, Forkhill, Crossmaglen
Around by the gap of Mount Norris and home by Blackwater again
Where girls are so fair and so pretty; none better you'll find near or far
But where are the boys that can court them like the boys from the County Armagh! *Chorus*

I Once Loved A Lass

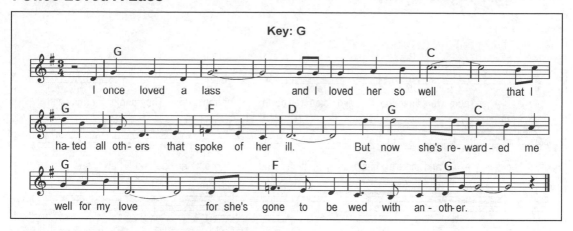

When I saw my love walk through the church door
With groom and bride maidens they made a fine show
And I followed them in with my heart full of woe
For now she is wed to another

When I saw my love a-sit down to dine
I sat down beside her and poured out the wine
I drank to the lassie that should have been mine
But now she is wed to another

The men in yon forest, they ask it of me
How many strawberries grow in the salt sea?
And I ask of them back with a tear in my eye
How many ships sail in the forest?

So dig me a grave and dig it so deep
And cover me over with flowers so sweet
And I will turn in for to take a long sleep
And maybe in time I'll forget her

They dug him a grave and they dug it so deep
They covered him over with flowers so sweet
And he has turned in for to take a long sleep
And maybe by now he's forgotten

97

The Raggle-Taggle Gypsy

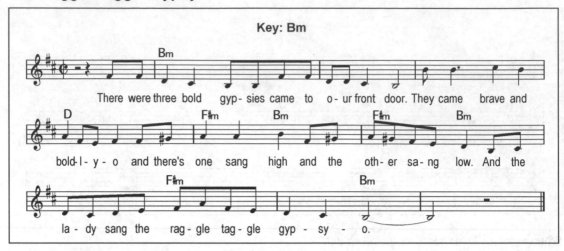

Key: Bm

There were three bold gyp-sies came to o-ur front door. They came brave and bold-l-y-o and there's one sang high and the oth-er sa-ng low. And the la-dy sang the rag-gle tag-gle gyp-sy-o.

They sang sweet and they sang low and fast her tears began to flow
She laid down her silken gown her golden rings and all her show

It was upstairs and downstairs the lady went; put on her suit of leather-o
And it was the cry all around the door "She's away with the raggle-taggle gypsy-o"

It was late that night when the lord came home enquiring for his lady-o
The servant's voice rang around the house; "She is gone with the raggle-taggle gypsy-o"

"Oh then saddle for me, me milk white steed; the black horse is not speedy-o
And I will ride and I'll seek me bride whose away with the raggle-taggle gypsy-o"

Oh then he rode high and he rode low; he rode north and south also
But when he came to a wide open field it is there that he spotted his lady-o

"Oh then why did you leave your house and your land; why did you leave your money-o
And why did you leave your newly wedded lord to be off with the raggle-taggle gypsy-o"

"Yerra what do I care for me house and me land and what do I care for money-o
And what do I care for my newly-wedded lord; I'm away with the raggle-taggle gypsy-o"

"And what do I care for my goose-feathered bed with blankets drawn so comely-o
Tonight I'll sleep in the wide open field all along with the raggle-taggle gypsy-o"

"Oh for you rode east when I rode west; you rode high and I rode low
I'd rather have a kiss from the yellow gypsy's lips than all your land and money-o"

The Jolly Beggarman

He would not lie within the barn nor yet within the byre
But he would in the corner lie down by the kitchen fire
And then the beggar's bed was made of good clean sheets and hay
And down beside the kitchen fire the jolly beggar lay. *Chorus*

The farmer's daughter she got up to bolt the kitchen door
And there she saw the beggar standing naked on the floor
He took the daughter in his arms and to the bed he ran
"Kind sir", she said "Be easy now, you'll waken our good man". *Chorus*

"O no, you are no beggar man, you are some gentleman
For you have stole my maidenhead and I am quite undone"
"I am no lord, I am no squire, of beggars I be one
And beggars they be robbers all and you are quite undone". *Chorus*

The farmer's wife came down the stairs, awakened from her sleep
She saw the beggar and the girl and she began to weep
She took the bed in both her hands and threw it at the wall
Says "Go you with the beggar man, your maidenhead and all!". *Chorus*

Weile Walia

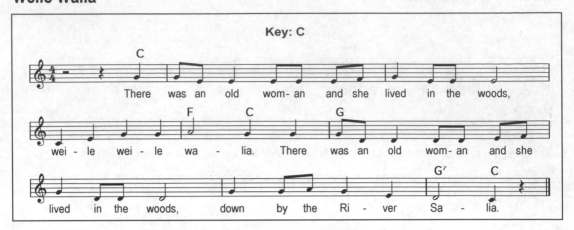

She had a baby three months old, weile, weile, walia
She had a baby three months old, down by the River Salia

She had a pen-knife long and sharp, weile, weile, walia
She had a pen-knife long and sharp, down by the River Salia

She stuck the pen-knife in the baby's heart, weile, weile, walia
She stuck the pen-knife in the baby's heart, down by the River Salia

Three loud knocks came a-knocking on the door, weile, weile, walia
Three loud knocks came a-knocking on the door, down by the River Salia

Two policemen and a man, weile, weile, walia
Two policemen and a man, down by the River Salia

"Are you the woman what killed the child", weile, weile, walia
"Are you the woman what killed the child", down by the River Salia

They tied her hands behind her back, weile, weile, walia
They tied her hands behind her back, down by the River Salia

The rope was pulled and she got hung, weile, weile walia
The rope was pulled and she got hung, down by the River Salia

And that was the end of the woman in the woods, weile, weile, walia
And that was the end of the baby too, down by the River Salia

Come To The Bower

Will you come to the land of O'Neill and O'Donnell
Of Lord Lucan of old and immortal O'Connell
Where Brian drove the Danes and St. Patrick the vermin
And whose valleys remain still most beautiful and charming. *Chorus*

You can visit Benburb and the storied Blackwater
Where Owen Roe met Munroe and his chieftains did slaughter
You may ride on the tide o'er the broad majestic Shannon
You may sail 'round Lough Neagh and see storied Dungannon. *Chorus*

You can visit New Ross, gallant Wexford and Gorey
Where the green was last seen by proud Saxon and Tory
Where the soil is sanctified by the blood of each true man
Where they died, satisfied, their enemies they would not run from. *Chorus*

Will you come and awake our lost land from its slumbers
And her fetters we will break; links that long are encumbered
And the air will resound with 'Hosannas' to greet you
On the shore will be found gallant Irishmen to meet you. *Chorus*

The Rose Of Allendale

Where e'er I wandered, east or west; though fate began to lour
A solace still she was to me in sorrow's lonely hour
When tempests lashed our lonesome barque and tore her shiv'ring sail
One maiden form withstood the storm; 'twas the Rose of Allendale. *Chorus*

And when my fevered lips were parched on Africa's hot sands
She whispered hopes of happiness and tales of distant lands
My life has been a wilderness, unblessed by fortune's gale
Had fate not linked my lot to hers, the Rose of Allendale. *Chorus*

Danny Boy
(Also known as "The Derry Air")

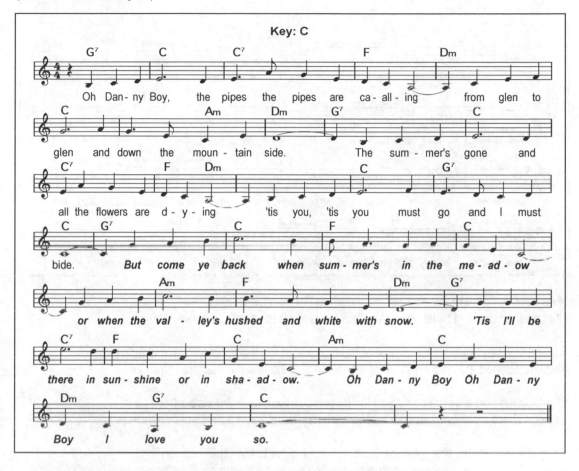

And when ye come and all the flowers are dying; and if I'm dead, as dead I well may be
You'll come and find the place where I am lying; and kneel and say an 'Avé' there for me
Chorus

And I shall hear, though soft you tread above me; and all my grave will warmer, sweeter be
If you will bend and tell me that you love me; then I shall sleep in peace till you're with me
Chorus

As I Roved Out

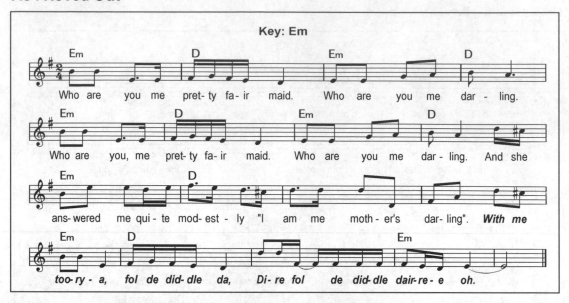

Key: Em

Who are you me pret-ty fa-ir maid. Who are you me dar - ling.

Who are you, me pret-ty fa-ir maid. Who are you me dar - ling. And she

ans-wered me qui-te mod-est-ly "I am me moth-er's dar-ling". **With me**

too-ry - a, fol de did- dle da, Di- re fol de did- dle dair-re- e oh.

"And will you come to my mother's house when the moon is shining clearly (repeat)
I'll open the door and I'll let you in and divil the one will hear us". *Chorus*

So I went to her house in the middle of the night when the moon was shining clearly (repeat)
And she opened the door and she let me in and divil the one did hear us. *Chorus*

She took me horse by the bridle and the bit and she led him to the stable (repeat)
Saying "There's plenty of oats for a soldier's horse to eat them if he's able". *Chorus*

Then she took me by the lily-white hand and she led me to the table (repeat)
Saying "There's plenty of wine for the soldier boy to drink it if your able". *Chorus*

I got up and I made me bed and I made it nice and easy (repeat)
Then I took her up and I laid her down saying "Lassie are you able?" *Chorus*

And there we lay till the breaking of the day and divil the one did hear us (repeat)
Then I arose and put on me clothes, saying "Lassie, I must leave you". *Chorus*

"And when will you return again and when will we be married?" (repeat)
"When broken shells make Christmas bells, then will we be married". *Chorus*

Henry My Son

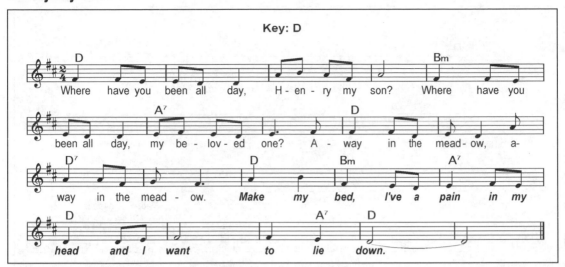

And what did you have to eat, Henry my son
What did you have to eat, my beloved one
Poisoned beads, poisoned beads. *Chorus*

What colour were those beads, Henry my son
What colour were those beads, my beloved one
Green and yellow, green and yellow. *Chorus*

What will you leave your mother, Henry my son
What will you leave your mother, my beloved one
A woollen blanket, a woollen blanket. *Chorus*

What will you leave your children, Henry my son
What will you leave your children, my beloved one
The keys of heaven, the keys of heaven. *Chorus*

And what will you leave your sweetheart, Henry my son
What will you leave your sweetheart, my beloved one
A rope to hang her, a rope to hang her. *Chorus*

Banna Strand

'Twas on Good Friday morning all in the month of May. A German ship was signalling beyond out in the bay. With twenty thousand rifles all ready for to land. But no answering signal did come from the lonely Banna Strand

"No signal answers from the shore" Sir Roger sadly said
"No comrades here to meet me; alas they must be dead
But I must do my duty and today I mean to land"
So in a small boat rowed ashore on the lonely Banna Strand

Now the R.I.C. were hunting for Sir Roger high and low
They found him in McKenna's Fort; said they "You are our foe"
Said he "I'm Roger Casement, I come to my native land
And I mean to free my countrymen on the lonely Banna Strand"

They took Sir Roger prisoner and they sailed to London Town
And in the Tower they laid him; a traitor to the Crown
Said he "I am no traitor" but on trial he had to stand
For bringing German rifles to the lonely Banna Strand

'Twas in an English prison that they led him to his death
"I'm dying for my country" he said with his last breath
They buried him in British soil far from his native land
And the wild waves sang his requiem on the lonely Banna Strand

The Bard Of Armagh

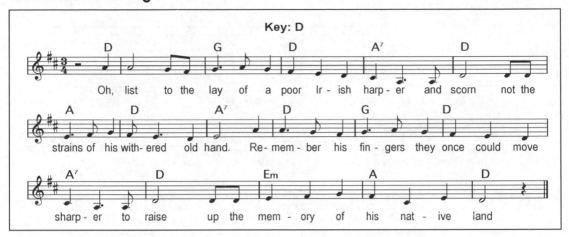

When I was a young lad King Jamie did flourish
And I followed the wars with my brogues bound with straw
And all the fair colleens from Wexford to Durrish
Called me Bold Phelim Brady, the Bard of Armagh

How I love for to muse on the days of my boyhood
Though four score and three years have flitted since then
Still it gives sweet reflections as every young joy should
For light-hearted boys make the best of old men

At pattern or fair I could twist my shillelagh
Or trip through a jig with me brogues bound with straw
Whilst all the pretty maidens around me assembled
For Bold Phelim Brady, the Bard of Armagh.

Although I have travelled this wide world over
But Erin's my home and a parent to me
Then oh, let the ground that my old bones will cover
Be cut from the soil that is trod by the free

And when Sergeant Death in his cold arms shall embrace me
Oh lull me to sleep with sweet 'Erin go Brath'*
By the side of my young wife, dear Kathleen, oh place me
Then forget Phelim Brady, the Bard of Armagh

*Pronounced "Erin go bra" (Ireland forever!)

The Glendalough Saint

(Verses and chorus have the same melody)

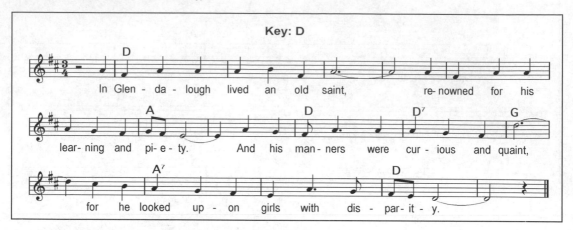

Fol-ol di lol-lol di lol-lay; fol-ol di lol-lol di lol-laddy
Fol-ol di lol-lol di lol-lay; fol-ol di lol-lol di lol-laddy

He was fond of reading a book when he could get one to his wishes
He was fond of casting his hook down among the young fishes. *Chorus*

One day he caught him a fish; he caught himself a fine trout, sir
When Kathleen from over the lake came to see what the monk was about, sir. *Chorus*

"Get out of me way" said the saint for I am a man of great piety
And me good manners I wouldn't taint to be mixing with female society. *Chorus*

Oh but Kathleen she wouldn't give in and when he went home to his rockery
He found she was seated therein a-polishing up his old crockery. *Chorus*

Well he gave the poor creature a shake and I wish that the peelers had caught him
For he flung her right into the lake and begorra she sank to the bottom! *Chorus*

The German Clockwinder

(Verses and chorus have the same melody)

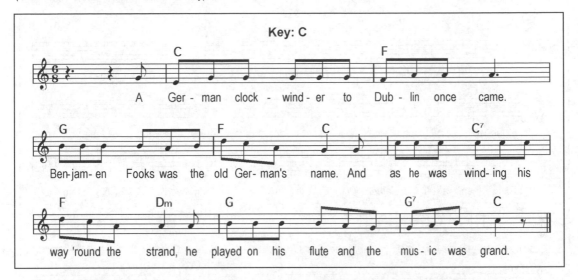

With me toor-a-lumma, toor-a-lumma, toor-a-lie-ay; toor-a-lie, oor-a-lie, orr-a-lie-ay
Toor-a-lumma, toor-a-lumma, toor-a-lie-ay; oor-a-lie, oor-a-lie, orr-a-lie-ay

Now there was a young lady from Grosvenor Square; who said that her clock was in need of repair
In walks the bold German and to her delight; in less than five minutes he had her put right
Chorus

Now as they were seated down on the floor; there started a very loud knock on the door
In walked her husband and great was his shock; to see the bold German wind up his wife's clock
Chorus

The husband says he "Oh wife, Mary Ann; don't let that bold German come in here again
He wound up your clock and left mine on the shelf; if your oul' clock needs winding I'll wind it myself!"
Chorus

The Shores Of Americay

I'm bid - ding fare - well to the land of my youth and the home that I love so well, and the moun - tains so grand in my own nat - ive land I'm bid ding them a - ll fare - well. With an a - ch - ing heart I will bid them a - dieu, to - mor - row I sail far a - way. O'er the r - ag - ing foam for to seek out a home on the shores of Am - er - ic - ay.

And it's not for the want of employment I go, and it's not for the love of fame
Or that fortune so bright may shine over me and give me a glorious name
No it's not for the want of employment I go o'er the stormy and perilous sea
But to seek a new home for my own true love on the shores of Americay

And when I am bidding my final farewell the teardrops like rain will blind
To think of my friends in my own native land and the home that I'm leaving behind
And If I'm to die in a foreign land and be buried so distant away
No fond mother's tears will be shed o'er my grave on the shores of Americay

The Nightingale

(Verses and chorus have the same melody)

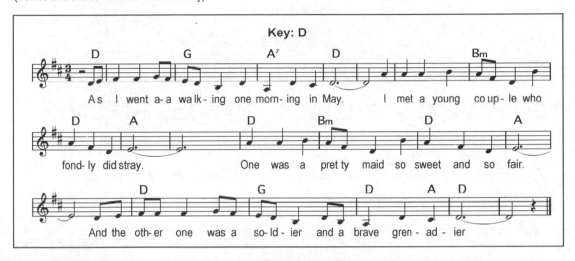

As I went a-a walk-ing one morn-ing in May. I met a young coup-le who fond-ly did stray. One was a pret ty maid so sweet and so fair. And the oth-er one was a so-ld-ier and a brave gren-ad-ier

And they kissed so sweet and comforting as they clung to each other
They went arm-in-arm along the road like sister and brother
The went arm-in-arm along the road till they came to a stream
And they both sat down together for to hear the nightingale sing

From out of his knapsack he took a fine fiddle
And he played her such a merry tune with a hi-diddle-diddle
And he played her such a merry tune that the trees they did ring
And they both sat down together for to hear the nightingale sing. *Chorus*

Oh soldier, handsome soldier will you marry me
Oh no said the soldier that never can be
For I have a wife at home in my own country
And she is the sweetest little flower that you ever did see. *Chorus*

Now I am off to India for seven long years
Drinking wine and strong whiskey instead of cold beers
And if ever I return again it will be in the spring
And we'll both sit down together for to hear the nightingale sing. *Chorus*

Sam Hall

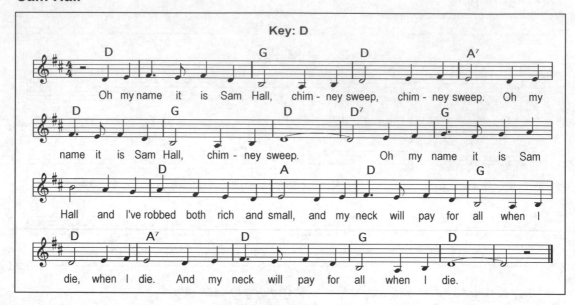

Oh they took me to Coote Hill in a cart, in a cart
Oh they took me to Coote Hill in a cart
Oh they took me to Coote Hill and 'twas there I made my will
For the best of friends must part; so must I, so must I
For the best of friends must part; so must I

Up the ladder I did grope; that's no joke, that's no joke
Up the ladder I did grope; that's no joke
Up the ladder I did grope and the hangman pulled the rope
And ne'er a word I spoke; tumbling down, tumbling down
And ne'er a word I spoke; tumbling down

(Repeat first verse)

Three Score And Ten

(Verses and chorus have the same melody)

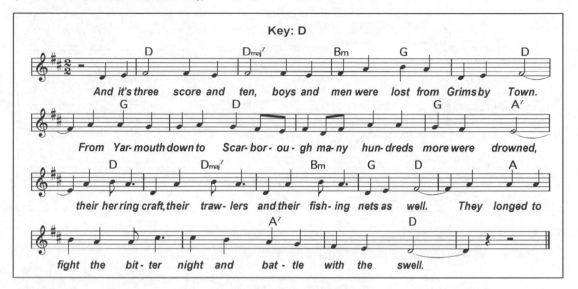

Now me thinks I see a host of gallant craft, spreading their sails a-lea
As down the Humber they did lie, bound for the cold North Sea
Me thinks I see a wee small craft, and crew with hearts so brave
They want to earn their daily bread all on the restless waves. *Chorus*

October night brought such a dreadful sight, 'twas never seen before
There were masts and yards of broken spars washed up along the shore
There was many a heart of sorrow, there was many a heart so brave
There was many a true and noble lad who found a watery grave. *Chorus*

Old Woman From Wexford

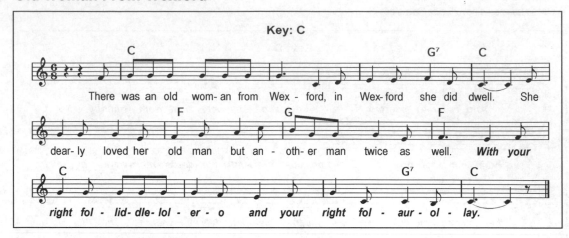

One day she went to the doctor for some medicine for to find
Says she "Will ye give me something for to make me old man blind". *Chorus*

"Feed him eggs and marrowbones and make him suck them all
And it won't be very long before he won't see you at all". *Chorus*

The doctor wrote a letter and he signed it with his hand
And he sent it to the old man so that he would understand. *Chorus*

She fed him eggs and marrowbones and made him suck them all
And it wasn't very long before he couldn't see the wall. *Chorus*

Said he "I'd like to drown myself but that would be a sin"
Said she "I'll come along with you and help to push you in". *Chorus*

The woman she stepped back a bit to rush and push him in
But the old man quickly stepped aside and she went tumbling in. *Chorus*

How loudly she did holler oh how loudly she did call
"Yerra hold your whist old woman sure I can't see you at all". *Chorus*

Now eggs and eggs and marrowbones may make your old man blind
But if you want to drown him you must creep up from behind. *Chorus*

All For Me Grog

(Verses and chorus have the same melody)

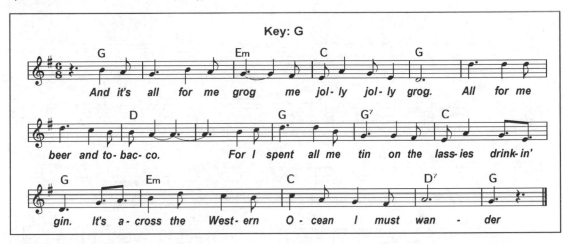

Where are me boots, me noggin' noggin' boots
They're all gone for beer and tobacco
For the heels are worn out and the toes are kicked about
And the soles are lookin' out for better weather. *Chorus*

Where is me shirt, me noggin' noggin' shirt
It's all gone for beer and tobacco
For the collar is all worn and the sleeves they are all torn
And the tail is lookin' out for better weather. *Chorus*

I'm sick in the head and I haven't been to bed
Since I first came ashore from me slumber
For I spent all me dough on the lassies, don't you know
Far across the Western Ocean I must wander. *Chorus*

Tipping It Up To Nancy

Key: D

There was a wom-an in o-ur town, a wom-an you all know well. She dear-ly loved her hus-band but an-oth-er man twice as we-ll. *With me right finn-ick-an-air-ee-o, me tip finn-ick a wall, with me right finn-ick-an-air-ee-o, we're tipp-in' it up to Nan-cy.*

She went down to the chemist shop some remedies for to find
"Have you anything in your chemist shop to make me old man blind?" *Chorus*

"Give him eggs and marrowbones and make him suck them all
And before he has the last one sucked he won't see you at all". *Chorus*

She gave him eggs and marrowbones and made him suck them all
Before he had the last one sucked he couldn't see the wall. *Chorus*

"If in this world I cannot see, then here I cannot stay
"I'd rather go and drown meself"; says she "I'll show the way". *Chorus*

She led him to the river and she led him to the brim
But sly enough of the old lad it was him that shoved her in. *Chorus*

"Oh husband dear I'm going to drown don't leave me here behind!"
"Yerra shut your mouth" the old lad said, "sure don't ye know I'm blind". *Chorus*

Home By Bearna

We won't go home across the fields, the big thornins could stick in your heels
We won't go home across the fields, we'll go home by Bearna
We won't go home around the glen, for fear your blood might rise again
We won't go home around the glen, but we'll go home by Bearna

We won't go down the milk boreen, the night is bright we might be seen
We won't go down the milk boreen, but we'll go home by Bearna
We won't go home across the bog for fear we might meet Kearney's dog
We won't go home across the bog, but we'll go home by Bearna

Boulavogue

He led us on 'gainst the coming soldiers and the cowardly yeomen we put to flight
'Twas at the Harrow the boys of Wexford showed Bookey's regiment how men could fight
Look out for hirelings King George of England; search every kingdom where breathes a slave
For father Murphy of County Wexford sweeps o'er the land like a mighty wave

We took Camolin and Enniscorthy and Wexford, storming, drove out our foes
'Twas at Slieve Coilte our pikes were reeking with crimson blood of the beaten Yoes
At Tubberneering and Ballyellis full many a Hessian lay in his gore
Ah, Father Murphy, had aid come over, the Green Flag floated from shore to shore

At Vinegar Hill o'er the pleasant Slaney our heroes vainly stood back to back
And the Yeos of Tullow took Father Murphy and burned his body upon the rack
God grant you glory brave Father Murphy and open heaven to all your men
The cause that called you may call tomorrow in another fight for the Green again

Sweet Carnlough Bay

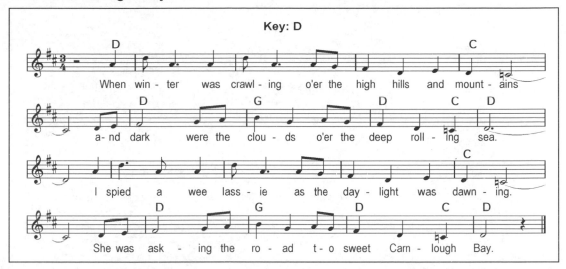

I said "My fair lass, I surely will tell you
The road and the number of miles it will be
And if you consent I'll convey you a wee bit
And I'll show you the road to sweet Carnlough Bay"

"You turn to the right and go down by the churchyard
Cross over the river and down by the sea
We'll stop at Pat Hamill's and have a wee drop there
Just to help us along to sweet Carnlough Bay"

Here's a health to Pat Hamill, likewise the fair lassie
And to all you young lads who are listening to me
Ne'er turn your back on a bonnie young lassie
When she's asking the road to sweet Carnlough Bay

The Lark In The Morning

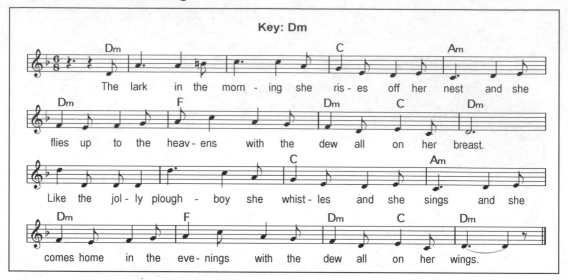

Key: Dm

The lark in the morn - ing she ris - es off her nest and she
flies up to the heav - ens with the dew all on her breast.
Like the jol - ly plough - boy she whist - les and she sings and she
comes home in the eve - nings with the dew all on her wings.

Oh Roger the ploughboy he is a dashing blade
He goes whistling and singing in yonder leafy shade
He met with dark-eyed Susan; she's handsome I declare
And she is far more enticing than the birds all in the air

As they were coming home from the rakes of the town
The meadow being all mown and the grass had been cut down
And as they should chance to tumble all in the new-mown hay
"Oh, it's kiss me now or never" this bonnie lass would say

When twenty long weeks were over and had passed
Her mammy asked the reason why she thickened 'round the waist
"It was the pretty ploughboy" this lassie then did say
"For he asked me for to tumble all in the new-mown hay"

Here's a health to you ploughboys wherever you may be
That like to have a bonnie lass a-sitting on each knee
With a pint of good strong porter he'll whistle and sing
And the ploughboy is as happy as a prince or a king

The Rose Of Mooncoin

(Verses and chorus have the same melody)

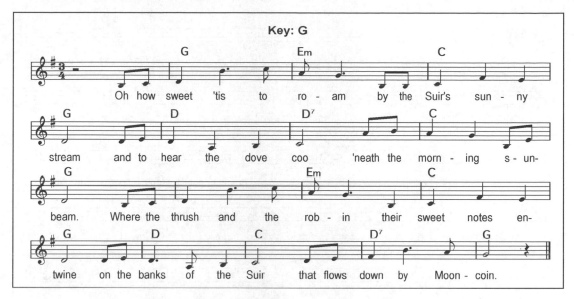

Flow on lovely river, flow gently along
By your waters so sweet sounds the lark's merry song
On your green banks I'll wander where first I did join
With you, lovely Molly, the Rose of Mooncoin

Oh Molly, dear Molly, it breaks my fond heart
To know that we shortly forever must part
I'll think of you Molly while sun and moon shine
On the banks of the Suir that flows down by Mooncoin. *Chorus*

She has sailed far away o'er the dark rolling foam
Far away from the hills of her dear Irish home
Where the fisherman sports with his small boat and line
By the banks of the Suir that flows down by Mooncoin. *Chorus*

Oh then here's to the Suir with its valleys so fair
Where oft times we wandered in the cool morning air
Where the roses are blooming and the lilies entwine
On the banks of the Suir that flows down by Mooncoin. *Chorus*

Nora

The golden dewed daffodils shone, Nora and danced in the breeze on the lea
When I first said I loved only you, Nora and you said you loved only me
The birds in the trees sang their songs, Nora of happier transports to be
When I first said I loved only you, Nora and you said you loved only me.

Our hopes they have never come true, Nora; our dreams they were never to be
Since I first said I loved only you, Nora and you said you loved only me
The violets are withered and gone, Nora; I cry for the years as they flee
Since I first said I loved only you Nora and you said you loved only me.

The Butcher Boy

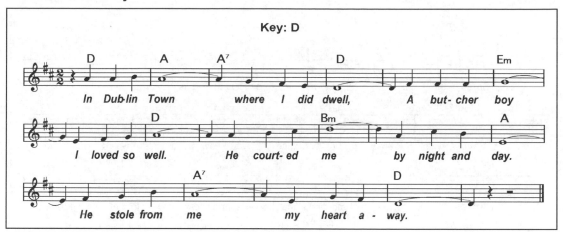

Key: D

In Dub-lin Town where I did dwell, A but- cher boy
I loved so well. He court- ed me by night and day.
He stole from me my heart a - way.

I wish my baby it was born, and smiling on its daddy's knee
And my poor body to be dead and gone, with the long green grass growing over me

I'll go upstairs and make my bed;   "What's there to do?" my mother said
My mother she has followed me, and saying "what's to come of thee?" **Chorus**

"Oh mother dear you little know, my pain and sorrow and my woe
Go get a chair and sit me down; with pen and ink I'll write it down"

Her father he came home that night, enquiring for his heart's delight
He went upstairs the door he broke, and found her hanging by a rope. *Chorus*

He took a knife and cut her down, and in her bosom these lines he found
"Oh what a foolish girl was I, to give my heart to a butcher boy"

"Go dig my grave both wide and deep; put a marble stone at my head and feet
And in the middle a turtle dove, so the world might know I died for love. *Chorus*

The Rocks Of Bawn

My shoes they are all worn and my stockings they are thin
My heart is always trembling now for fear they might give in
My heart is always trembling now from the clear daylight till the dawn
And I never will be able to plough the Rocks of Bawn

My curse upon you Sweeney boy, you have me nearly robbed
You're sitting by the fireside now, your feet upon the hob
You're sitting by the fireside now from the clear daylight till the dawn
And you never will be able to plough the Rocks of Bawn

Rise up gallant Sweeney, and get your horses hay
And give them a good feed of oats before they start away
Don't feed them on soft turnip sprigs that grow on yon green lawn
Or they never will be able to plough the Rocks of Bawn

I wish the Sergeant-Major would send for me in time
And place me in some regiment while in my youth and prime
I'd fight for Ireland's glory now from the clear daylight till the dawn
Before I would return again to plough the Rocks of Bawn

The Holy Ground

And now the storm is raging and we are far from the shore
And the night is dark and dreary and our happy thoughts no more
And the good ship she is tossed about and the rigging is all torn
But still I live in hope to see the Holy Ground once more, FINE GIRL YOU ARE! *Chorus*

And now the storm is over and we are safe and well
We will go into a public house and we'll eat and drink our fill
And we'll drink strong ale and porter and make the rafters roar
And when our money is all spent we'll go to sea once more, FINE GIRL YOU ARE! *Chorus*

The Croppy Boy

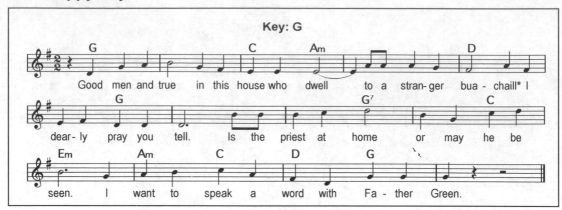

The youth has entered an empty hall, with lonely sounds does his light foot fall
And the gloomy chamber is cold and bare, with a vested priest in a lonely chair

The youth has knelt to tell his sins; "Nomine Dei" the youth begins
At "mea culpa" he beats his breast; in broken murmurs he speaks the rest

"At the siege of Ross did my father fall, and at Gorey my loving brothers all
I alone am left of my name and race; I will go to Wexford to take their place"

"I cursed three times since last Easter Day; at Mass-time once I went to play
I passed the churchyard one day in haste and forgot to pray for my mother's rest"

"I bear no hate against living thing, but I love my country above my King
Now father bless me and let me go, to die if God has ordained it so"

The priest said naught, but a rustling noise made the youth look up in a wild surprise
The robes were off and in scarlet there sat a Yeoman captain with a fiery glare

With fiery glare and with fury hoarse, instead of a blessing he breathed a curse
"'Twas a good thought, boy, to come here and shrive, for one short hour is your time to live"

"Upon yon river three tenders float; the priest's in one if he isn't shot
We hold this house for our lord and King, and amen say I, may all traitors swing"

At Geneva Barracks that young man died and at Passage they have his body laid
Good people who live in peace and joy, now breath a prayer for the croppy boy

*Pronounced "voukill" (boy)

Joe Hill

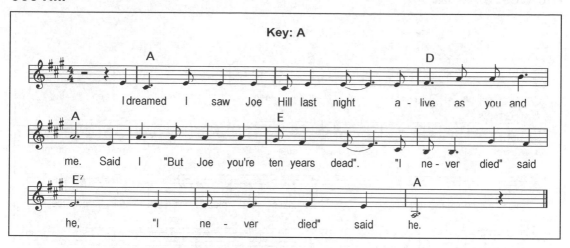

"In Salt Lake City, Joe", said I, him standing by my side
"They framed you on a murder charge". Said Joe "I never died"
Said Joe "I never died"

"The copper bosses shot you, Joe; they filled you full of lead"
"Takes more than guns to kill a man" said Joe, "and I ain't dead"
Said Joe "and I ain't dead"

And there he stood as large as life and smiling with his eyes
Said Joe "what they forgot to kill went on to organise
Went on the organise"

From San Diego up to Maine in every mine and mill
Where working men defend their rights it's there you'll find Joe Hill
It's there you'll find Joe Hill

(Repeat first verse)

The West's Awake

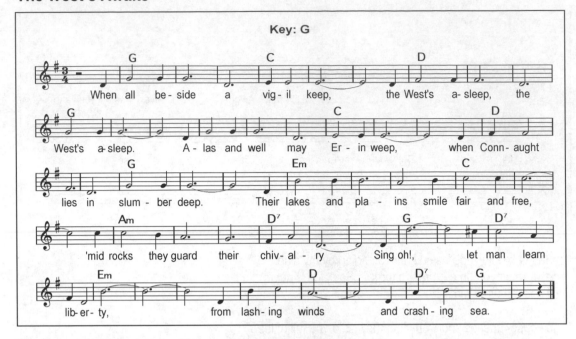

Key: G

When all be-side a vig-il keep, the West's a-sleep, the West's a-sleep. A-las and well may Er-in weep, when Conn-aught lies in slum-ber deep. Their lakes and pla-ins smile fair and free, 'mid rocks they guard their chiv-al-ry Sing oh!, let man learn lib-er-ty, from lash-ing winds and crash-ing sea.

That chainless wave and lovely land; Freedom and Nationhood demand
Be sure the great God never planned; for trodden slaves a home so grand
For long a proud and haughty race; honoured and sentinelled the place
Sing, Oh! Not e'en their sons' disgrace; can quite destroy their glory's trace

For often in O'Connor's van; to triumph dashed each Connaught clan
As fleet as deer the Normans ran; through Curlew's Pass and Ardrahan
And later times saw deeds so brave; and glory guards Clanricard's grave
Sing, Oh! They died their land to save; at Aughrim's plains and Shannon's wave

And if when all a vigil keep; the West's asleep, the West's asleep
Alas as well may Erin weep; that Connaught lies in slumber deep
But hark, a voice like thunder spake; the West's awake, the West's awake
Sing, Oh! Hurrah, let England quake; we'll watch till death for Erin's sake

Carrickfergus

My childhood days bring sad reflections of happy times spent long ago
My boyhood friends and my own relations have all passed on now like the melting snow
So I'll spend my days in endless roving; soft is the grass, my bed is free
Ah, to be back now in Carrickfergus, on that long road down to the sea

Now in Kilkenny, it is reported there are marble stones as black as ink
With gold and silver I would transport her but I'll sing no more now till I get a drink
I'm drunk today and I'm seldom sober, a handsome rover from town to town
Ah, but I'm sick now and my days are over, so come all ye young lads and lay me down

Old Maid In The Garret

Key: G

I have of-ten heard it said by my fath-er and my moth-er that
go-ing to a wed-ding was the mak-ings of an-oth-er. Well if this be
so then I'll go with-out a bid-ding. Oh it's kind Prov-id-ence, won't you
send me to a wed-ding! *For it's oh de-ar me, how will it*
be if I die an old maid in the gar - ret!

Oh now there's my sister Jean; she's not handsome nor good-looking
Scarcely sixteen and a fella she was courting
Now she's twenty-four with a son and a daughter
Here am I forty-five and I've never had an offer. *Chorus*

I can cook and I can sew, I can keep the house right tidy
Rise up in the morning and get the breakfast ready
There's nothing in this wide world would make me half so cheery
As a wee fat man who would call me his own dearie. *Chorus*

Oh come landsman or come townsman, come tinker or come tailor
Come fiddler, come dancer, come ploughman or come sailor
Come rich man, come poor man, come fool or come witty
Come any man at all who would marry me for pity. *Chorus*

Oh well I'm away to home for there's nobody heeding
There's nobody heeding to poor old Annie's pleading
For I'm away home to my own wee-bit garret
If I can't get a man then I'll surely get a parrot. *Chorus*